ANTISOCIAL
BORDERLINE
NARCISSISTIC
& HISTRIONIC
WORKBOOK

Treatment Strategies For Cluster B Personality Disorders

Daniel J. Fox, PhD author of *The Clinician's Guide to the Diagnosis and Treatment of Personality Disorders*

"Personality disorders are common in clinical practice, but helpful resources are not. Dr. Fox answers the call with a workbook that will deepen your understanding of the assessment and treatment of Cluster B personalities, with a dedicated emphasis on handouts and worksheets that guide therapy and provide a catalyst for change. Enthusiastically recommended!"

-Lane Pederson, PsyD, LP, DBTC, author of
The Expanded Dialectical Behavior Therapy Skills Training Manual

"Full of concrete tools to make successful progress in treatment! The research provides a great foundation for the use of the materials and Dr. Fox has pulled from multiple resources to create tools clinicians and clients can both use to promote wellness and growth. I have found that the use of the workbook can be applicable in nearly every session I have with someone battling with a Cluster B personality disorder. After applying the concepts in this workbook I have found that Cluster B clients are not the same beasts in treatment that they were in the past."

-Susan Barris, PhD

"Insightful for the therapist and easy-to-use with clients. The worksheets are very effective in assisting with a more accurate diagnosis of Cluster B personality types and, even more importantly, understanding the therapists own responses to the client. This workbook is also helpful when needing to incorporate more tangible and structured treatment approaches into therapy. The DBT worksheets are easy to follow and use "client friendly" language and concepts."

-Meagan N. Houston, PhD

"The collection of exercises for the clinician and the client are practical, useful, and empirically driven. This is a well written, easy to read, and thorough guide providing a framework and a level of confidence for the clinician facing the challenges of treating severe personality disorders."

-Kristy Dromgoole, PhD

"This rich resource assists the clinician in avoiding errors in diagnosis that can often occur when working with clients with complex symptom presentations. Dr. Fox presents the material in a straightforward, easy to digest, manner that can be appreciated and utilized by all practitioners. Clinicians, regardless of their training background or theoretical orientation, will find this to be an invaluable resource in the diagnosis and treatment of Cluster B personality disorders."

-Mary Madison Eagle, PhD

"Dr. Fox's passion for this subject shines through in the workbook format. This workbook can serve as both a reference and a helpful tool for gathering information. Dr. Fox's style of writing is clear and concise. I was able to take in the information quickly and see how useful the worksheets could be."

-Kristin A. Lue King, MSW

Copyright © 2015 by Daniel J. Fox, Ph.D.

Published by
PESI Publishing & Media
PESI, Inc
3839 White Ave
Eau Claire, WI 54703

Cover: Amy Rubenzer
Editing: Blair Davis
Layout: Bookmasters & Amy Rubenzer

ISBN: 9781559570183

Printed in the United States of America.

Library of Congress Cataloging-in-Publication Data

Fox, Daniel J., Psychologist.
  Antisocial, borderline, narcissist & histrionic workbook : treatment strategies for cluster B personality
disorders / Daniel J Fox, Ph.D.
     pages cm
  Includes bibliographical references.
  ISBN 978-1-55957-018-3
1. Personality disorders. 2. Personality disorders--Treatment. I. Title. II. Title: Antisocial, borderline,
narcissist and histrionic workbook.
  RC554.F69 2015
  616.85'81--dc23
                    2015029495

PESI
Publishing
& Media
www.pesipublishing.com

This book is dedicated to my three heartbeats: my wife, Lydia, and my two children, Alexandra and Sebastian.

Table of Contents

About the Author

 **Daniel J. Fox, Ph.D.,** has been specializing in the treatment and assessment of individuals with personality disorders for more than 16 years in the state and federal prison system, universities, and private practice. He is a licensed psychologist in the state of Texas and author of *The Clinician's Guide to The Diagnosis and Treatment of Personality Disorders* and several articles on personality, ethics, and neurofeedback. His specialty areas include personality disorders, ethics, and emotional intelligence. Dr. Fox has been teaching and supervising students for the past 13 years at various universities across the country, including West Virginia University, Texas A&M University, University of Houston, Sam Houston State University, and Florida State University.

He is currently a staff psychologist at the Federal Detention Center in Houston, Texas, and Adjunct Assistant Professor at University of Houston. He also maintains a private practice that specializes in assessment and treatment of difficult clients. Dr. Fox has given numerous workshops and seminars domestically and internationally on ethics and personality disorders, personality disorders and crime, emotional intelligence, burnout prevention, managing mental health within the prison system, and other related topics.

For more information on Dr. Fox, visit his website at www.drdfox.com.

Who This Workbook Is For and How to Use It

Many clinicians feel confused by or helpless in the face of the severe pathology associated with antisocial, narcissistic, histrionic, and borderline personality disordered clients. These four disorders make up Cluster B of the personality disorders in the Diagnostic and Statistical Manual of Mental Disorders, currently in its fifth edition (American Psychiatric Association [APA], 2013). The reason these four disorders are contained within a cluster is due to overlap in symptoms and presentation. This overlap further confounds treatment for the frontline clinician, as symptoms are expressed from various aspects of the pathology along a spectrum. Most clients are at different points on the spectrum and will not meet criteria for the full disorder. For example, many clients will display borderline personality disorder traits but not to the extent to merit the full diagnosis. This workbook is designed to treat individuals who meet full criteria as well those who display traits and are on the spectrum of any of the Cluster B disorders.

Due to the inherent complexity of the presentation of such disorders, there are multiple approaches a clinician can use to attenuate symptomatology. This workbook is designed to provide assistance to the frontline clinician who may be stuck or feel that he or she is out of options when working with this complex group of individuals. The workbook pulls from multiple therapeutic modalities that include interpersonal, object relations, cognitive-behavioral, and Dialectical Behavioral Therapy.

The first section provides useful tools and information on antisocial, narcissistic, histrionic, and borderline personality disorders that can aid in directing treatment, identifying risk and protective factors, and determining which Cluster B personality disorders or traits are present. The remaining parts of the workbook contain detailed worksheets and exercises for each of the four Cluster B spectrums. Due to the overlap in symptoms across the four disorders, many of the worksheets and exercises can be useful for individuals who have traits on more than one spectrum. For example, a client who has comorbid traits along the borderline and antisocial spectrums would benefit from worksheets and exercises from both of these sections.

The make-up of each section includes information on the specific personality disorder and subtypes along its spectrum, followed by specialized worksheets and exercises for each. In addition, each of the four specific personality disorder sections includes a worksheet on attachment, as this is a critical factor to address when working with any individual on a personality disorder spectrum. The final section includes worksheets based on DBT. This section stands alone, as these worksheets can be useful for individuals with any of the Cluster B features. **Scoring and answer keys can be found in Appendix A.**

Part One
Critical Components

Personality Disorders — They're Not Going Anywhere

Society within the United States is exceptionally complex. It represents the customs and values of cultures all across the world, and the resultant composition is certainly unique. From this comes individuals with varying degrees of functioning; some of these people are functioning outside the norms of society and their specific cultures. An individual's maladaptive functioning can become so ingrained and solidified into a person's identity that he or she develops maladaptive qualities that have negative social and economic consequences; we call these personality disorders. Personality disorders and their associated traits are increasing in frequency. I once had a client tell me that "our society is like raising a chicken. A chicken is designed to provide one egg a day, but society demands that they produce multiple eggs, so they push harder." Thus, society has put us in a position where we are asked to produce various results within a high-pressure system. Does this mean that high pressure, intense demands, and expectations that surmount our human design are the cause of personality disorders? Simply put, no. There are multiple theories as to why personality disorders exist and why some people operate in an abnormal fashion outside of cultural expectations and norms.

The prevalence rate of personality disorders in the United States is estimated to be 9.1% (Lenzenweger et al., 2007). This means that there are an estimated 28,548,864 people meeting criteria for personality disorders, with 4.0% meeting criteria for Cluster A (paranoid, schizoid, and schizotypal personality disorders), 2.0% meeting criteria for Cluster B (antisocial, narcissistic, borderline, and histrionic personality disorders), and 4.2% meeting criteria for Cluster C (obsessive-compulsive, avoidant, and dependent personality disorders) (Huang et al., 2009). Interestingly, the cluster with the lowest prevalence is the one that requires the greatest amount of therapeutic resources.

We focus so much on Cluster B clients because they are most likely to seek treatment and tend to experience the greatest degree of clinical impairment. The individuals in Clusters A and C tend to fly below the radar, live in their parents' homes, work in solitary careers, such as computer programming or online work, and stay out of the spotlight in most cases.

As our society has sped up, we have kept pace with the production of personality disorders. Why is that? Look at the personality traits on the next page and and see if you have experienced or displayed many or all of the traits listed at some time in your life.

The fact that all of us around the world have displayed most or all of these traits at one time or another does not mean we are all personality disordered. Instead, it means that we display many of these traits based on situational circumstances, such as idealizing a new romantic partner, having a temper outburst due to road conditions (a.k.a. road rage), and exhibiting particular odd mannerisms that you show to your significant other or closest friends. Individuals with personality disorders lack the ability to adjust their behavior based on the situation and continue to demonstrate maladaptive traits in a variety of contexts.

Personality Traits	
• Idealizing	• Needing to be special or unique
• Devaluing	• Failures in empathy
• Vanity	• Cruelty
• Temper outbursts	• Infidelity
• Boredom	• Working too hard or too little
• Seductiveness	• Hypervigilance
• Rapidly shifting emotions	• Ideas of reference
• Devastation in the face of criticism	• Odd mannerisms
• Wanting to be too intimate or distant	• Being irresponsible
• Needing advice about little things	• Being too bossy
• Being too autonomous	• Being withdrawn
• Having trouble getting started	• Hating being alone
• Feeling devastated when a relationship ends	• Wanting acceptance but fearing rejection
• Being perfectionistic	• Resenting others' control
	• Being critical of authorities

This leads us to the definition of personality disorders that we will use throughout this workbook, proposed by Lorna Smith Benjamin:

The inability to adjust your behavior based upon the situation you are in

For example, Jimmy meets criteria for antisocial personality disorder. He acts out violently and takes advantage of people at work, when he is in prison, in his romantic relationships and friendships, and in treatment. He may garner varying degrees of immediate reward through these acts, but he does not adjust his behavior in situations in which doing so could be advantageous to him and help him achieve genuine success. He lacks the ability to alter his behavior across contexts to get his needs met in an appropriate manner.

Due to our society downplaying the importance of coping mechanisms and instead promoting a "what is in it for me?" attitude, the rate of personality disorders continues to grow. Although this is a simplification of a complex problem, it reveals a critical need for a workbook directed at treatment for clients with Cluster B personality disorders and those individuals along their spectrums.

Before we can engage in treatment, we have to make certain that what we are diagnosing is actually a personality disorder and not a chronic or acute situational reaction. The definition given previously provides us with general guidance, but the diagram that follows helps you identify whether your client in fact has a personality disorder by identifying the five critical factors across all personality disorders.

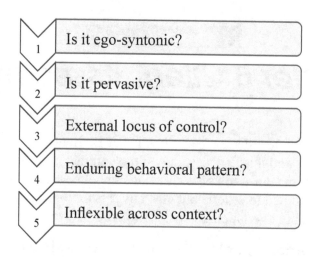

1	Is it ego-syntonic?
2	Is it pervasive?
3	External locus of control?
4	Enduring behavioral pattern?
5	Inflexible across context?

Note: If you are uncertain as to which personality disorder you may be working with, as there is so much overlap within clusters, utilize the Cluster B Client Assessment on the following pages to help you.

Is it ego-syntonic? When your client engages in a particular behavior, typically with a negative outcome, does he or she experience regret? Ego-syntonic behavior does not bother the individual. For example, your client may have a sexual relationship with his or her significant other's father. If this is behavior is ego-syntonic, he or she does not experience regret, doubt, or internal conflict associated with the behavior.

Is the behavior pervasive? We want to be sure that the behavior occurs across multiple contexts, such as work, home, romantic relationships, and employment/academic relationships. For example, your client tends to yell and scream when agitated, whether at work, school, or home, and to his or her boss, co-worker, significant other, or friend. The individual with a personality disorder expresses his or her agitation regardless of the situation or with whom he or she is interacting.

Does he or she possess an external locus of control? Having an external locus of control is when an individual experiences an event, whether good or bad, and attributes the cause to uncontrollable outside factors, such as the environment, other people, or a higher power. For example, your histrionic client loses his job due to provocative behavior and making a pass at his boss. He states that he was really fired because the boss got embarrassed and everyone in the office was jealous of his good looks—they were just trying to find a reason to fire him.

Is this an enduring behavioral pattern? An enduring behavioral pattern is one that occurs regardless of an identifiable trigger. For example, your client with borderline personality disorder almost always sabotages relationships after one week due to feeling too close to the identified object, significant other, friend, or co-worker.

Is he or she inflexible across contexts? Individuals with personality disorders tend to display inflexibility in response, regardless of internal factors or consequences. For example, your client with antisocial personality disorder tends to act out violently whether he or she is interacting with a store clerk, police officer, or young child, knowing that his or her behavior could, or most likely will, lead to incarceration, loss of a loved one, or loss of employment.

Assessing for these five components will help you to accurately determine whether your client does indeed have a personality disorder. If he or she does not meet all five criteria, you should reassess to determine whether a genuine personality disorder is present. You should never diagnose an individual who is under the influence of or withdrawing from medication or substances with a personality disorder, as substances can cause various symptoms and complicate the clinical picture.

Cluster B Client Assessment

When working with personality disorders, especially Cluster B clients, we know there is a high probability of treatment errors and misdiagnosis due to the complexity of symptom presentation. The worksheet that follows is designed to assist clinicians in better determining the Cluster B diagnosis. The statements here are not limited to criteria but also cover symptoms and behaviors that are highly indicative of the four distinct but overlapping Cluster B disorders.

Directions: Circle the time period(s) in which the behavior presented itself for your client. If it was never displayed, circle *Never*. If it was displayed in the past (meaning not currently), circle *Past*. If a behavior is currently being displayed, circle *Present*. The scoring key can be found in Appendix A.

1. Unsentimental or unemotional in outlook	Never	Past	Present
2. Insensitive toward others	Never	Past	Present
3. Angry or distressed over minor separation or relationship stressor	Never	Past	Present
4. Tends to express or describe emotions as larger than they really are	Never	Past	Present
5. Tends to be shallow and insincere	Never	Past	Present
6. Engages in self-sabotaging behaviors	Never	Past	Present
7. Craves novelty and stimulation in situations and relationships	Never	Past	Present
8. Tends to do things suddenly and without careful thought	Never	Past	Present
9. Takes advantage of others to gain concern from caretakers	Never	Past	Present
10. Tends to see relationships as much more intimate than they actually are (and feels intimacy quickly; e.g., met someone yesterday, and they are their new best friend)	Never	Past	Present
11. Lack of self-value or purpose	Never	Past	Present

12. Willing to look weak or fragile to gain attention	Never	Past	Present
13. Likes to win the attention or admiration of others but does not have serious feelings for them	Never	Past	Present
14. Concerned only with what is obvious or apparent	Never	Past	Present
15. Short-term (i.e., lasting hours) psychotic symptoms due to stressful emotional reaction	Never	Past	Present
16. Self-image is intact	Never	Past	Present
17. Moves between dependency and emotional seductiveness/manipulation to control partner	Never	Past	Present
18. Excessive feeling of self-respect and deserving to be respected by other people for some achievement	Never	Past	Present
19. Has difficulty understanding and/or sharing another person's experiences and emotions	Never	Past	Present
20. Attempts to impress others by being special or appearing special but this is not based in reality or practical	Never	Past	Present
21. Does not know who he or she is or what he or she believes in	Never	Past	Present
22. Looks down on others for possessing emotional awareness and understanding of the feelings of other people	Never	Past	Present
23. Discounts the feelings and values of others	Never	Past	Present
24. Has an appearance that gets them noticed to obtain love, care, and/or attention	Never	Past	Present
25. Difficulty achieving emotional intimacy and depth in romantic/sexual relationships (tends to be superficial)	Never	Past	Present
26. Unfairly or cynically uses another person or group for profit or advantage	Never	Past	Present
27. Needs constant attention, praise, and gifts from others	Never	Past	Present
28. Continuous and/or intensive fear of significant other leaving and never returning	Never	Past	Present

Structure of Personality Disorders

Personality tends to be seen as a linear construct, but in actuality, it is much more complex. When we think of an individual's personality we tend to try to simplify it into one or two words. He's *moody*, or she's *antisocial*. When we consider the psychopathology involved in a personality disorder, this leaves much necessary information unintentionally ignored.

The complexity of a personality disorder should be examined from two points, a surface structure and a core structure. The surface structure is what is overt and obvious; for example, anger, jealousy, or promiscuity. When clinicians treat only surface structure content they tend to become frustrated, get lost in the pathology, and miss the mark in treatment due to inaccurately and untimely engaging in an intervention. Core content includes the surface content but examines intrinsic motivators that cause the surface behaviors. If you address core content, you attenuate surface behaviors and also awaken defense mechanisms. You have had this experience, likely not knowing it.

When you are working with a client who has a personality disorder and you tap into core content, you see that he or she becomes defensive, angry, flirtatious, highly emotional, etc., depending on which personality disorder is present. In session, you may have tried to lessen the defense by pulling back and refocusing on the surface content, but as therapy continues, you will note that these emotional issues keep happening. It is much more conducive to long-term change and time management to address the core content. This workbook is designed to assist you in that process.

Case Study

Let's examine this in greater detail. Betty is a sample complex client:

> *Betty is a 22-year-old woman who is having severe difficulty making and keeping friends. Many of her friends are frustrated with her strong need to control them and her demanding style. Additionally, she always "dictates what they do." If her friends want to do something other than what Betty wants, Betty will often become angry and "ditch" them. However, her friends enjoy spending time with her because she is usually the life of the party and never backs down from a dare.*
>
> *She will often drive recklessly, has two DWIs, and may shoplift if things get "too boring." Sometimes Betty is slow to respond to her friends' texts or e-mails, and will stay at home for days at a time with no overt reason. When she is not around her friends, Betty often cries and searches the internet for her next boyfriend or romantic encounter.*
>
> *She calls these "romantic encounters," as she is not highly selective about who it is and engages in this behavior only to "press flesh." Betty's longest relationship was five months, and that ended because her partner caught her making a pass at his father.*

Using a linear approach to look at a client like Betty the clinician would see the following:

Surface Structure
Obsessive-Compulsive Personality Disorder (OCPD): Intractable with friends Demanding Need for control **Impulse Control Disorder:** Drives recklessly, DWIs Life of party Loves a dare Shoplifts Promiscuous **Major Depressive Disorder (MDD):** Does not respond to friends Inside for days Crying spells

When we look at core content, Betty's symptoms are still present, but the underlying pathology is clearer:

Core Structure
Borderline Personality Disorder (BPD): Intractable with friends Demanding Need for control Drives recklessly, DWIs Life of party Loves a dare Shoplifts Promiscuous Does not respond to friends Inside for days Crying spells

Betty's surface structure is misleading. She will meet criteria for obsessive-compulsive personality disorder, impulse control disorder, and major depressive disorder, but the approach to treating these disorders, individually or together, takes therapy off track. If we treat the surface diagnoses, we will attempt to lessen perfectionism, examine urges and behavioral consequences, and reduce sadness, disengagement, and her negative view of the world. During this course of treatment, we may tap into some core issues, but when we do, we are often surprised by defenses that arise and we are potentially taken off guard. However, when we examine the symptoms and what motivators are driving the surface behaviors, we see that borderline personality disorder is a better diagnosis. The core issues for Betty that indicate borderline personality are abandonment fears, emptiness, and comfort in chaos.

By addressing the core issues, therapy moves forward. The therapist is prepared for the defenses of idealization and devaluation, self-neglect, possible self-mutilation, etc. Treating core structure encourages change but also makes therapy a more complicated process, because it is up to the therapist, with participation from the client, to uncover the core structure and lessen its impact by replacing the maladaptive behaviors with positive and self-affirming behaviors.

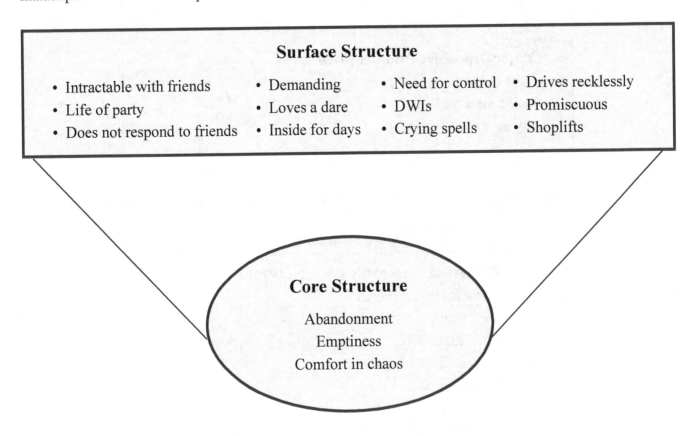

From a treatment standpoint, the core structure is what we are primarily attending to in treatment, as it comprises the intrinsically motivating factors that continue to cause problems in Betty's life.

Next Steps

When core structure changes, so does surface structure and overt behaviors. Use the worksheet that follows to examine core and surface structure with your clients.

Personality Structure

Directions: In the box labeled "Behaviors," please list your behaviors that give you a sense of satisfaction. These behaviors are not good or bad, they are just behaviors. Your first thought is usually the best. In the oval labeled "Motivations," list what motivates you to engage in these behaviors—the reasons *why* you do them. Do not edit your responses.

Behaviors

_____   _____
_____   _____
_____   _____
_____   _____
_____   _____
_____   _____

Motivations

_____   _____
_____   _____
_____   _____
_____   _____
_____   _____
_____   _____
_____   _____

Critical Factors in the Treatment of Histrionic, Antisocial, Narcissistic, and Borderline Clients

The following exercise will help you to recognize the probable etiological experiences that are associated with each Cluster B personality type. You can compare your answers with identified high-probability past experiences that greatly influence the development of histrionic, antisocial, narcissistic, and borderline personality disorders found in Appendix A.

Directions: Under each Cluster B personality disorder type, put a check mark (✓) next to the etiological experience you believe a client with this type of disorder is likely to have had.

Histrionic Personality Disorder	Antisocial Personality Disorder
_____ Sexual abuse	_____ Sexual abuse
_____ Physical abuse	_____ Physical abuse
_____ Emotional abuse	_____ Emotional abuse
_____ Neglect	_____ Neglect
_____ Being bullied	_____ Being bullied
_____ Bullying others	_____ Bullying others
_____ Deliberate self-harm	_____ Deliberate self-harm
_____ Prolonged periods of misery	_____ Prolonged periods of misery

Narcissistic Personality Disorder	Borderline Personality Disorder
_____ Sexual abuse	_____ Sexual abuse
_____ Physical abuse	_____ Physical abuse
_____ Emotional abuse	_____ Emotional abuse
_____ Neglect	_____ Neglect
_____ Being bullied	_____ Being bullied
_____ Bullying others	_____ Bullying others
_____ Deliberate self-harm	_____ Deliberate self-harm
_____ Prolonged periods of misery	_____ Prolonged periods of misery

Client Experience

Directions: Below, each etiological experience is defined and a response is provided. Write in your client's experience with each responsive factor. For example, if your client with histrionic personality disorder experienced sexual abuse as a child, you would write, *Client X was often asked to parade around the house naked while her father and his friends watched and would "hoot and holler." This continued until age 16, when client left home.*

Not only does this exercise help you define the etiological experience, but it also provides various vantage points from which to see it. The preceding example is clearly an instance of sexual abuse, but it can also be classified as neglect. This helps to provide avenues for treatment that enable you to work with your client to resolve this issue. In the histrionic personality disorder section, worksheets on attachment, true self/false self, and the six levels of validation would be helpful in working with a client on past abuse issues.

Sexual Abuse: Forcing an individual to engage in undesired sexualized behavior. Sexual abuse can also include indecent exposure (e.g., displaying of the genitals, female breasts, etc.) to a child or of a child with intent to gratify an adult's sexual desires or to intimidate or groom the child, asking or pressuring a child to engage in sexual activities, displaying pornography to a child, or using a child to produce child pornography.

Physical Abuse: The use of physical force that may result in bodily injury, physical pain, or impairment. This may include but is not limited to such acts as striking (with or without an object), hitting, beating, pushing, shoving, shaking, slapping, kicking, pinching, and burning. In addition, inappropriate use of drugs and physical restraints, force-feeding, and physical punishment of any kind also are examples of physical abuse.

Emotional Abuse: The infliction of anguish, pain, or distress through verbal or nonverbal acts. This includes but is not limited to verbal assaults, insults, threats, intimidation, humiliation, and harassment. Additionally, emotional abuse can include treating someone like an infant; isolating an individual from his or her family, friends, or regular activities; giving an individual the "silent treatment"; and/or forced social isolation.

Neglect: The refusal or failure to fulfill any part of a person's obligations or duties to someone in one's care. Neglect typically means the refusal or failure to provide an individual with such life necessities as food, water, clothing, shelter, personal hygiene, medicine, comfort, personal safety, and/or other essentials included in an implied or agreed upon responsibility to that person.

Being Bullied: The recipient of force, threat, or coercion causing feelings of abuse, intimidation, or being aggressively dominated by another person on a repeated basis. The perception by the individual being bullied is of an imbalance of social or physical power.

Bullying Others: The use of force, threat, or coercion to abuse, intimidate, or aggressively dominate another person that is often repeated and habitual. The perception by the bully or by others is of an imbalance of social or physical power. Behaviors often used to assert such domination include verbal harassment/threat, physical assault, or coercion.

Deliberate Self-Harm: The deliberate and direct destruction/alteration of body tissue without suicidal intent, but resulting in injury severe enough for tissue damage to occur.

Prolonged Periods of Misery: A state of extreme unhappiness due to difficult circumstances or distress or suffering caused by need, deprivation, poverty, or other mental or emotional stressors. The cause or source of the distress occurs for an extended period of time (e.g., hours, days, months).

Personality Disorder Risk and Protective Factors

There are multiple risk and protective factors that contribute to the development and avoidance of personality disorders. In treatment, we often overlook examining the risk and protective factors, but these are critical components that can hinder or promote therapeutic success.

A risk factor is a variable associated with an increased probability of developing a particular disease or disorder, in this case, a personality disorder. The precise cause of personality disorders is not known, but certain factors seem to increase the risk of developing or triggering personality disorders. Risk factors are often evident in childhood and put the individual on a trajectory of pathology to develop a personality disorder later in life.

The more risk factors an individual has, the greater the probability he or she will develop a personality disorder. There is no single factor that is causal for developing a particular personality disorder. Personality disorders are typically derived from several adverse environmental experiences in combination with genetic factors (Huff, 2004). The seven risk factors (Lenzenweger, 2010; "Personality Disorders," Mental Health America, 2013; Silk, 2003) included in the checklist that follows are not hard-and-fast rules but singular components that are additive to the overall probability of developing a personality disorder.

Just as there are risk factors that promote personality disorders, there are protective factors that insulate an individual from developing them. These protective factors can also be used during the course of treatment as resources to help your client get through difficult times. Knowledge of your client's protective factors can enhance the treatment that is being done to control and attenuate the behavioral expression of the personality disorder(s), whether it is borderline, antisocial, histrionic, and/or narcissistic personality disorder.

Protective factors come from many different aspects of an individual's life and his or her genetic makeup (Huff, 2004). Protective factors can also be developed from the client's past, present, and current therapeutic experience. Utilizing aspects of the protective factors that are present assists the therapist during times of crisis and when therapy becomes highly stressful. These are client resources that the therapist can use to help the client move through difficult times and that can and should be enhanced during the course of treatment.

One of the most critical protective factors is having a secure attachment base. Secure attachment has been linked with acceptable emotional expression, strong peer relations, positive social skills, greater understanding of other people's emotions, greater sharing, less aggressive and antisocial behavior, closer friendships, being well liked by others, and better academic performance.

Case Study

The following case study illustrates how to best use the information gathered from the checklist (on page 18) in treatment.

Yolanda is a 27-year-old woman who has been in treatment for the past five months and has been accurately diagnosed with histrionic personality disorder. Her parents passed away following a home invasion when she was seven-years-old. She was then placed in foster homes, where she was abused and found that the best way for her to feel safe was to be "in the spotlight." She has difficulty maintaining employment, friendships, and romantic relationships.

Yolanda completed the Risk and Protective Factors Checklist and identified the following: verbal, physical, and sexual abuse during childhood, loss of parents through death or traumatic divorce during childhood, family history of personality disorders or other mental illness, being well liked by others, good grades in school, ability to read well, and exposure to positive role models.

Yolanda has several risk factors we need to be aware of, as she has just lost another job. She was let go because she slept with her boss in the hopes of earning a very high-profile promotion after being at the job for only three months. She tells her therapist that losing this promotion is just like losing her parents and being sexually abused all over again because she feels lost and forgotten. You know that her father was diagnosed with major depressive disorder and had Cluster B traits. Yolanda tells her therapist that she feels as though she cannot continue on this path and that her future is becoming more uncertain and "blurry." The therapist mentions her ability to meet new people, how she is often liked by others, and how she is able to learn new skills and create opportunities for herself. As Yolanda and her therapist discuss these issues, the therapist asks her about her positive role models. Yolanda states that she sees her therapist as a positive role model with whom she feels connected, and that that she is connected to her and that she can be open and honest when she loses opportunities and when life becomes "blurry."

The case study illustrates the key factors that are exacerbating and attenuating Yolanda's issues. The most salient portion of the checklist in this example is that Yolanda marked those factors herself—the therapist did not have to spend time in treatment looking for risk and protective factors. The checklist helped save time in treatment and also provided useful data to both Yolanda and the therapist to prevent what could have been a significant deterrent to therapeutic success.

Next Steps

The Risk and Protective Factors Checklist can be given directly to the client, or the therapist can fill it out for the client. An alternative method is for both client and therapist to fill it out separately and then compare what factors they each indicated. This provides an opportunity for client and therapist to discuss risk and protective factors that are impacting the client currently and may illuminate the root of symptoms present in the client's life.

In the checklist, factors related to secure attachment are indicated by double asterisks (**) and risk factors are indicated with one asterisk (*).

Risk and Protective Factors

Directions: Put a check mark (✓) in the box next to the factor(s) listed here that has occurred in your life. Some of these factors are from your childhood, whereas others are from what is going on now and from your therapeutic experience. Once you have completed the form, return it to your therapist so you both can review it to identify areas of focus during treatment.

☐ A family history of personality disorders or other mental illness *

☐ Ability to find benefit in adverse experiences

☐ Ability to read well **

☐ Positive social support

☐ Verbal, physical, or sexual abuse during childhood*

☐ Therapeutic relationship optimism

☐ Loss of parents through death or traumatic divorce during childhood*

☐ Strong peer relations**

☐ Positive emotional experiences

☐ Positive social skills**

☐ Greater understanding of others' emotions**

☐ Not often aggressive**

☐ Well liked by others**

☐ Good grades in school**

☐ Life satisfaction

☐ Involvement in organized religion or sense of spirituality

☐ Strong family relations

☐ Close friendships

☐ Unstable or chaotic family life during childhood*

☐ Participation in structured activities

☐ Exposure to positive role models

☐ Steady employment

☐ Low socioeconomic status*

☐ Ability to accurately determine threatening situation

☐ Accurate challenge appraisal

☐ Accurate self-control appraisal

☐ Acceptable emotional expression**

☐ Ability to find meaning in experiences

☐ Acceptance of self/others

☐ Being diagnosed with a childhood conduct disorder*

☐ Greater sharing**

☐ Avoidance of negative self/others

☐ Good physical health

☐ Neglect during childhood*

Part Two
Antisocial Personality Disorder Spectrum

Antisocial Personality and Its Subtypes

Antisocial Personality Disorder (ASPD) is composed of rule violation, disregard for and violation of the rights of others, and a long history of rule breaking. A common misconception is that everyone in prison has ASPD. This is simply not true. For example, in one study of 320 newly incarcerated offenders, only 113 (35%) met criteria for ASPD (Black et al., 2010). There are many antecedents of ASPD and its well-known subsets, sociopathy and psychopathy.

Two possible antecedents to ASPD are Conduct Disorder (CD) and Oppositional Defiant Disorder (ODD). Research shows that 90% of children diagnosed with CD had a previous diagnosis of ODD (Loeber et al., 1993). ODD and CD have many similar risk factors, and individuals with both disorders tend to present with disruptive behaviors. Research has suggested that ODD may be a developmental precursor to and milder variant of CD. As with all disorders, this is not a hard-and-fast rule. Approximately 25% of children with ODD will go on to eventually receive a diagnosis of CD (Loeber et al., 1993). However, research has shown a link between CD and ASPD in adults. This link is so strong that in order to qualify for ASPD as an adult "there is [must be] evidence of a conduct disorder with onset before age 15 years, (APA, 2013, p.659)." Some individuals do stop their asocial development at CD and never "graduate" to ASPD. Zoccolillo and colleagues found that only 25% to 40% of individuals with CD go on to develop ASPD. As with the development of any disorder, personality disorders included, there is no one pathway. However, a history of ODD and then CD increases the probability of later development of ASPD. But it does not end there.

Sociopathy and psychopathy have been seen as variants of a broader disorder of acting out and misbehavior known as ASPD. Individuals who are considered sociopaths can be described as "persons whose undersocialized character is due primarily to parental failures rather than inherent peculiarities of temperament". One who is considered a psychopath can be described as "an individual in whom the normal processes of socialization have failed to produce the mechanisms of conscience and habits of law abidingness that normally constrain antisocial impulses" (Lykken, 2006). Further distinction of these two underlying factors is beyond the scope of this section.

The trajectory and differentiation of expression from ODD to CD to ASPD to the variant forms that include sociopathy and psychopathy are shown in the following diagram.

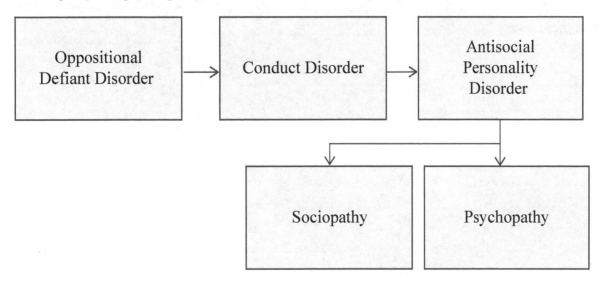

As depicted here, not everyone diagnosed with ASPD is a sociopath or a psychopath. Some individuals only meet criteria for the more general distinction, ASPD. Critical distinctions exist between ASPD, sociopathy, and psychopathy, which are presented in the following table.

Antisocial Personality Disorder	Sociopathy	Psychopathy
• Perpetual rule breaking and disregard for the rights of others. • Limited social skills and social engagement abilities. • Likelihood toward impulsive or opportunistic criminal behavior, excessive risk taking, impulsive or opportunistic violence. • Unlikely to harm family members and friends on purpose.	• Socially skilled. • Varied predisposition to violence. • Behavior can be erratic and situationally prone to violence. • Likelihood toward impulsive or opportunistic criminal behavior, excessive risk taking, impulsive or opportunistic violence. • Likely to appear superficially appropriate in social relationships and is often a social predator. May appear to empathize with close friends or family; will report feeling guilty if they hurt people close to them.	• Likely to lack social skills. • High likelihood of violence if it serves his or her needs. • Genetic component and lack of startle response. • Behavior typically controlled, though may seem impulsive. • Likelihood toward premeditated crimes with calculable risks, criminal opportunism, fraud, calculated or opportunistic violence. • Difficulty maintaining normal relationships. Values self-serving relationships. Potential to hurt family and friends without feeling guilty.

Working with and managing ASPD and its subtypes will continue to be a challenge for the frontline clinician. Making an accurate diagnosis is critical to managing in-session violence, working to identify secondary gain, dislodging the "wrong patient syndrome," and addressing many of the other complex issues that go along with treating this complex set of disorders. This workbook is designed to address and treat these issues.

Antisocial Personality Disorder
Homicidal Triad

The homicidal triad, or MacDonald Triad, is based on the work of forensic psychiatrist John MacDonald and his article "The Threat to Kill." The triad is composed of the following factors.

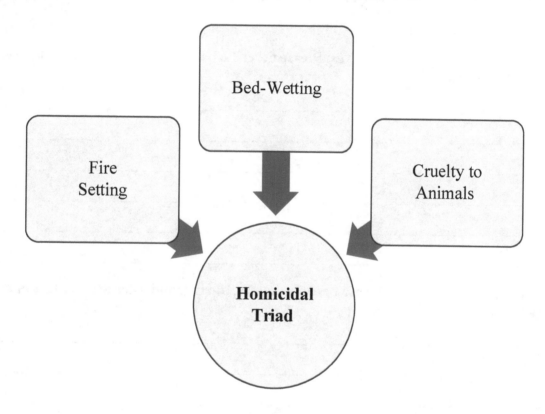

The triad is most indicative of an individual who, as a child, was under prolonged stress and had poor coping mechanisms or a developmental disability. Individuals with ASPD are known to have poor coping skills and a thwarted developmental trajectory. The homicidal triad should be viewed as an indicator that a client has serious issues worthy of clinical attention and is at a higher risk of moving from misbehavior or acting out to CD, antisocial traits, or a full-blown ASPD diagnosis.

Identification of past behaviors comprising the homicidal triad can provide invaluable information when working with individuals along the antisocial spectrum. It can indicate a lack of remorse, sensation seeking, and other critical components that may be present in the client's life.

Next Steps

The Behaviors Worksheet that follows is to be given to the client to address each of the homicidal triad components to be specifically covered in treatment. Once your client has answered the questions, discuss each in session. Recognize that strong indicators in each of the sections warrant further work in addressing ASPD traits. Please read through the ASPD section and find related worksheets (e.g., Behavior Replacement Worksheet, Conduct Disorder Worksheet, or Viewpoint Worksheet) to assist you in working further with your client on these clinically important issues.

Behaviors

Directions: Please answer the three questions listed below and describe what was going on in your life before, during, and after each incident in as much detail as you can. Remember, your therapist is there to help if you need it. Please be as honest and forthcoming as you can.

Have you:

Purposely *harmed an animal* ☐ No ☐ Yes: **Please describe before, during, and after the incident in as much detail as possible:**

_____

_____

_____

_____

_____

Purposely *set a fire* ☐ No ☐ Yes: **Please describe before, during, and after the incident in as much detail as possible:**

_____

_____

_____

_____

_____

After the age of 5, *had a problem with bed-wetting* ☐ No ☐ Yes: **Please describe how you felt or feel about having this problem in as much detail as possible:**

_____

_____

_____

_____

_____

Oppositional Defiant Disorder
Behavioral Replacement

Oppositional Defiant Disorder (ODD) is a possible precursor to CD and ASPD. Central characteristics include the following:

- Irritability
- Argumentativeness
- Vindictiveness

A pattern of these three central characteristics must be present for at least 6 months, according to the DSM-5. These behaviors typically drive temper tantrums, arguing with adults, refusing to comply with adult requests or rules, annoying others deliberately, blaming someone else for his or her mistakes or misbehavior, acting aggressively toward peers, academic problems, low self-esteem, sensitivity to feedback, and becoming annoyed easily. The child with ODD is likely to see his or her misbehaviors as a logical result of unreasonable demands being placed on him or her.

Individuals at the low end of the antisocial spectrum are likely to have had these feelings for some time and still harbor them as adults. As the child with ODD ages and continues to maintain these beliefs and perceptions, he or she can become more entrenched in these beliefs, justifying other misbehaviors, which creates greater adverse consequences for the client.

Next Steps

The Behavior Replacement Worksheet is designed to identify the central ODD characteristics, alternative behaviors, and applicable rewards to lessen the overall acting out and thwart movement along the antisocial spectrum. After your client has completed the Behavior Replacement Worksheet, go over the results to assess that the replaced behavior fits with the end result. It is not realistic to expect that simply telling a child who has ODD or a client who is on the low end of the antisocial spectrum that sitting down will result in less hassle from his or her teacher will bring about a change in behavior. Rewards for children with ODD or clients on the low end of the antisocial spectrum have to be clear, desired, and presented as close to the time of the new and alternative behavior as possible. The longer the client has to wait for the reward, the larger and more desirable the reward is going to have to be.

When the child with ODD or client on the low end of the antisocial spectrum has earned the reward, it can never be taken away due to new bad behavior. The client has earned it and should receive it. Other positive items or motivators can be taken away that have not been earned through this exercise. Once an earned reward can be taken away, it loses its motivating power.

A typical problem is that many parents or therapists of children with ODD or clients on the low end of the antisocial spectrum believe that parenting or teaching by punishment will correct the misbehavior. They need to be informed that this type of parenting or teaching will not only further encourage ODD behavior but may also add further justification for the behavior in the client's mind.

Behavior Replacement

Directions: On the following lines, list your behaviors that correspond to each of the characteristics below, indicate the alternative behavior, and finally, list the anticipated reward for engaging in the more appropriate behavior. Examples of each are presented.

Reminders:

- Rewards given cannot be taken away for new misbehavior.

- Time between alternative behavior expression and receipt of reward should be as short as possible. (Avoidance of punishment is not a reward.)

Irritability:

<u>Example</u> of irritability: *Michael gets angry when told by his teachers to sit down in class.*

<u>Alternative</u> to irritability: *Michael will be allowed a "cool-down break" designated by parent or teacher to self-soothe.*

<u>Reward</u> to lessen irritability: *Michael will be allowed an extra 30 minutes of "iPad time."*

_____

_____

_____

_____

_____

_____

_____

Argumentativeness:

<u>Example</u> of argumentativeness: *Michael will argue with me (mom) when asked to come inside for dinner if he is outside playing.*

<u>Alternative</u> to argumentativeness: *Michael is to state his disagreement in clear terms and identify the "who," "what," "where," "when," and "how" of his disagreement. (He may win sometimes, and that is good when presented appropriately.)*

<u>Reward</u> to lessen argumentativeness: *Michael earns dessert or points toward an app he wants.*

_____
_____
_____
_____
_____
_____
_____
_____
_____
_____

Vindictiveness:

Example of vindictiveness: *Michael will cut off his sister's doll's hair if she gets rewarded for a good grade and he does not, as he did not receive a good grade.*

Alternative to vindictiveness: *Michael will discuss or write a processing plan that will include: (1) his role in the incident, (2) the role of the other person in the incident, (3) the best solution to the incident, and (4) how to implement the best solution.*

Reward to lessen vindictiveness: *Michael earns extra time with friends outside.*

_____
_____
_____
_____
_____
_____
_____
_____
_____

Consistency is the key in identification, implementation, and reward to adjust ODD behavior.

Conduct Disorder

The goal of managing Conduct Disorder (CD) behavior is to replace negative behavior with more socially acceptable behavior. The problem is that CD behaviors tend to produce intrinsically satisfying rewards, whereas other behaviors do not. CD involves behaviors that include:

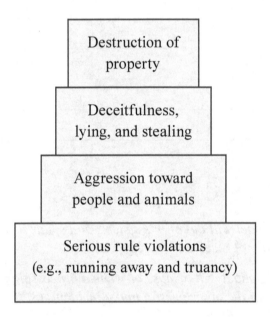

Conduct disorder is a precursor to and necessary criterion in diagnosing ASPD, and many of the behaviors associated with CD are seen in individuals along the antisocial spectrum. However, with proper treatment, ASPD is not a guaranteed result of CD. Adults can be diagnosed with CD. For individuals older than 18 years, a diagnosis of CD is given only if the criteria for ASPD are not met.

Next Steps

The Conduct Disorder Worksheet focuses on identifying goals, behaviors, motivating factor(s), consequences, and alternative behaviors that could be employed to better manage various situations.

Before using this worksheet, you should assess your client's willingness to engage in treatment and how motivated he or she is to change his or her CD behaviors. Individuals along the antisocial spectrum are often not motivated to change, as their misbehaviors are highly rewarding. What is intrinsically motivating your client for change?

There are many obstacles to learning and engaging in more prosocial behaviors in lieu of CD and antisocial behaviors, and it is important to identify the motivators of antisocial behaviors if they are to be changed. These are obstacles that impede success in relationships, academic settings, and employment settings. The most common CD behavior motivators are:

- **Aggressive behavior**
- **Feeling overwhelmed emotionally**
- **Failure to identify individual needs**
- **Fear**
- **Poisonous relationships**

Aggressive behavior for the client with CD or on the antisocial spectrum ranges from verbal abuse to the destruction of property. Individuals with aggressive behavior tend to be irritable, impulsive, and restless. Aggressive behavior is intentional, violates social norms, and causes a breakdown in a relationship. Aggressive behavior is a problem because it occurs frequently or as part of a pattern. The aggressive behavior of an individual with CD or on the antisocial spectrum is typically derived from an inability to control oneself from a misunderstanding of what behaviors are appropriate.

Feeling overwhelmed emotionally is when a client with CD or on the antisocial spectrum loses the ability to think and act rationally and perform in an efficient and functional manner. Being overwhelmed emotionally has many roots, which can include stress at home or work, past or current traumatic life experiences, and others.

Failure to identify individual needs can be a precursor to CD and antisocial behaviors. In many cases, the person with CD or on the antisocial spectrum feels he or she is being treated unfairly, is unheard, and is being easily dismissed. As the individual continually encounters these experiences, he or she minimizes his or her own feelings and replaces introspection with acting out.

Fear is a common root of CD and antisocial behaviors. Fear can be derived from the inability to control a situation or the perception of the inability to control a situation. Fear manifests in many different ways (e.g., overengagement or withdrawal), and for the client with CD or on the antisocial spectrum, it is typically paired with aggressive behavior.

Poisonous relationships are not uncommon for individuals with CD or on the antisocial spectrum. Poisonous relationships make it difficult to engage in prosocial behaviors due to the deleterious effects on the individual, the environment, and positive relationships. These relationships are not all negative, if they were, the client would self-select out of them. Instead, these relationships are rewarding, in that they are fun and exciting and validate the client's negative and harmful behaviors.

As a therapist, you must be aware of the old habits associated with CD and antisocial behavior, and in particular, which category your client falls into. The following worksheet includes five categories to log behaviors.

Conduct Disorder

Directions: This worksheet will help you break down current behaviors so that they can be evaluated, reasoned, and changed. In the first column, put the date the incident occurred, and in the second, the goal of the behavior. In the subsequent columns, write what motivated the behavior, the consequence of the behavior, and lastly, what alternative behavior could you have engaged in to better manage the situation. An example is provided.

Date	Goal	Behavior	Motivator	Consequence	Alternative Behavior
11/17/14	Get day off to attend daughter's birthday	Yelling at boss and walking out	Overwhelmed emotionally, Fear, Failure to identify individual needs	Fired from my job	Excuse myself, walk out, calm down, and re-engage in a calm and controlled manner

Antisocial Personality Disorder
Core and Surface Structure

The typical way of conceptualizing ASPD is based on its surface behaviors, which include criminal activity, aggressive control of others, manipulation, lack of remorse, poor insight into consequences, parental neglect, and rationalization of harmful behaviors. However, the internal/core structure is what drives the individual with ASPD to act in these ways. Typical treatment includes addressing surface behaviors within an individual therapy setting, but research has shown that the individual with ASPD does not respond well when only participating in individual therapy (Benjamin, 1996). The efficacy of treatment is contingent on where your client falls on the antisocial spectrum, depicted in the following diagram.

It is critical to be aware that treatment impact will vary depending on where your client falls on the antisocial spectrum. The further along on the spectrum, the more complicated the treatment will be and resistant to change your client is likely to be.

Next Steps

The Previous Experiences Worksheet is designed to assist you identify core and surface issues and addressing them in treatment. It is important to remember that working with core issues may bring up defenses in your client. When working with a client on the ASPD spectrum, defenses can be dangerous. The therapist is highly encouraged to monitor client responses when using with this worksheet to be aware of how tapping into core issues impacts your client's view of you and his or her world.

- **Core issues = defenses**
- **Be aware that working with core issues will cause client defenses to surface**
- **Be cautious and cognizant**

Benjamin notes four interpersonal history components (listed in the following chart) that are associated with typical interpersonal patterns in adult clients with ASPD and on the antisocial spectrum. These are the probable core issues for many individuals with ASPD and on the antisocial spectrum.

Interpersonal History Components			
Harsh, neglectful parenting	Sporadic, inconsistent humiliating parental control	Inept (questionable) parental caring	Disruptive child controls family via lack of parental control/follow through

These core experiences feed the surface presentation of an individual who does not care about others, is only out for himself or herself, and is not impacted by the world around him or her. In order to change the surface behaviors, the core structure has to be addressed and replaced with more positive conceptualizations of the world and prosocial behaviors. Again, be aware that treatment success is more likely with individuals on the lower end of the antisocial spectrum.

Previous Experiences

Directions: Please identify your life experiences that fit into the categories below. The purpose of this exercise is to gain therapeutic insight (for your therapist and yourself) to help correct current behaviors that could be making your life more difficult.

Harsh, neglectful parenting:

_____

_____

_____

_____

_____

Inconsistent/humiliating parental control:

_____

_____

_____

_____

_____

Questionable parental caring:

_____

_____

_____

_____

_____

Controlled the family through bad behavior:

_____

_____

_____

_____

_____

Attachment and the Antisocial Spectrum

Attachment is a critical component of how humans and animals connect with one another. Treating attachment issues is a complex process and involves identifying and working with the insecure attachment pattern and recreating a more secure attachment in its place. The therapeutic environment and relationship are ideal for doing this. To examine attachment and the antisocial spectrum we use the model devised by Bartholomew and Horowitz (1991) shown here.

	Positive View of Self	**Negative View of Self**
Positive View of Others	**Secure Attachment** Hopeful Satisfied Trusting Self-Disclosing	**Preoccupied Attachment** Hopeless Dissatisfied Trusting Self-Disclosing
Negative View of Others	**Dismissing Attachment** Hopeful Satisfied Distrusting Non-Disclosing	**Fearful Attachment** Hopeless Dissatisfied Distrusting Non-Disclosing

Working with attachment and the client on the antisocial spectrum brings about many complex issues. This is one of the chief reasons that working with this population can be so challenging. Bonding is exceptionally difficult for individuals along this spectrum because of their difficulty attaching to the therapist and tendency to utilize deceptive methods to get their needs met. It has been found that the ability to form an emotional bond, such as attachment, is suggestive of an individual being at the lower end of the antisocial spectrum, as compared with the more extreme cases, which include the genuine psychopath.

The individual on the antisocial spectrum has a dismissing attachment style, as discussed previously. Individuals within this attachment category tend to view others as negative and themselves as positive. They are hopeful and satisfied with themselves, while distrusting and non-disclosing to others. Noting that these are core issues for the individual on the antisocial spectrum, particular treatment methods need to be employed.

The therapist must be aware that an asymmetrical relationship will exist in which the attachment figure (the therapist) supplies the environment for secure attachment to develop rather than this security occurring in a more organic fashion over time. This imbalance will cause the therapist to feel that he or she is working harder trying to engage the client than he or she does with other clients who are not on the antisocial spectrum. The client on the antisocial spectrum expects others to see him or her as a lesser person with minimal value, and this will often be communicated to the therapist in verbal and nonverbal ways. Your handling of these "tests" will define the client's view of you and your skillset.

The core issues when working with clients on the antisocial spectrum are:

- Lack of genuineness

- Resistance to connecting with others

- Impaired ability to identify caring in others

- Difficulty building a sense of genuine self-concept

- Belief that others are unreliable

Next Steps

The following worksheet helps to address these core issues, but these are difficult problems for the individual on the antisocial spectrum to change. The further along on the spectrum the client is, the more complicated the treatment process will be because of the entrenched nature of the client's dismissing attachment style, which includes not being able to connect to others, belief in the unreliability of others, and emphasis on the value of self.

This worksheet works best when you have established a relationship that is honest and entails minimal manipulation and deceit. Ask your client to fill out the worksheet, and discuss the answers in a very open and non-threatening manner. The client will be highly sensitive to feedback, if he or she has answered honestly. Remember, every answer is a valuable one. If your client gives an answer that you know is false, that still provides useful data in treatment. All information, even a lie, is fodder for treatment. Your client's answers can be seen as a projective assessment.

Relational Trust and Security

Directions: Write your immediate thoughts after each sentence stem. *Do not edit your thoughts.* The first sentence stem in each pair reflects how you judge people for a particular trait. The second sentence stem in each pair facilitates your reflection on how you can change the judgement if it is negative, or how you can strengthen it if it is positive.

People are trustworthy when:

_____

_____

_____

_____

People can show they are trustworthy by:

_____

_____

_____

_____

You know you can connect with someone else when:

_____

_____

_____

_____

People show they are worthy of being connected with by:

_____

_____

_____

_____

People care when:

_____

_____

_____

_____

You show someone you care by:

_____

_____

_____

_____

People show how they feel about themselves by:

_____

_____

_____

_____

You show how you feel about yourself when:

_____

_____

_____

People can be counted on when:

_____

_____

_____

_____

You show you can be counted on by:

_____

_____

_____

_____

Antisocial Spectrum and Suicide Risk

Assessing suicide risk in clients on the antisocial spectrum is a difficult and complex clinical issue. Most suicide attempts by individuals along this spectrum are due to reactive aggressiveness, persistent criminality, and meeting criteria for ASPD (Bukstein et al., 1993). Frontline clinicians know that assessing suicidal behaviors is critical within this population and that 5% of individuals meeting criteria for ASPD will be suicide completers, while 11% are attempters (Frances, Fyer, & Clarkin, 1986).

Many critical components have been found that can indicate an increase in suicidal acting out. Critical factors include low well-being, achievement, and self-control and increased reactions to stress, self-removal from one's ingroup, and aggressive behavior (Verona, Patrick, & Joiner, 2001). Additional common factors include unhappiness with life, anxiety, extreme sadness, blunted emotions, and lack of social responsiveness.

Next Steps

The Perception Questionnaire contains 19 items that help you identify suicidal tendencies and ideation in your client on the antisocial spectrum, as well as protective factors. Answers indicate the probability of suicide risk and what factors are present to decrease the probability of a suicide attempt. It is important to collect information about these symptoms, as suicidal ideation and attempts can severely thwart treatment progress, interpersonal relationships, and employment. **The scoring key can be found in Appendix A.**

You should focus on the protective factors that are present during treatment, especially when difficulties arise and your client begins to discuss thoughts of self-harm. The more risk factors that are present, the greater the likelihood of suicidal acting out, and these matters should be addressed accordingly.

The following questionnaire is not a stand-alone tool and should never supplant clinical judgment or the need to intervene in cases in which you deem your client a threat to self or other. If you believe your client may be at risk of harming himself or herself or someone else, contact your local emergency room or law enforcement agency and follow recommended guidelines per your state's licensing board.

Perception

Directions: Please circle Agree or Disagree after each statement according to how it pertains to you.

1. I am seldom "really happy."	Agree	Disagree
2. I seldom get worried.	Agree	Disagree
3. I usually work hard enough to just get by.	Agree	Disagree
4. I prefer to turn the other cheek.	Agree	Disagree
5. I easily get upset.	Agree	Disagree
6. People treat me fairly.	Agree	Disagree
7. Life has given me a raw deal.	Agree	Disagree
8. I like to put in long hours to accomplish something.	Agree	Disagree
9. If someone crosses me, I will let him or her know about it.	Agree	Disagree
10. I am a happy person.	Agree	Disagree
11. I usually act before thinking.	Agree	Disagree
12. I feel blessed and happy.	Agree	Disagree
13. I am dissatisfied with my life.	Agree	Disagree
14. I like to have detailed plans before doing something.	Agree	Disagree
15. It is hard for me to feel my emotions.	Agree	Disagree
16. Life is great.	Agree	Disagree
17. I feel anxiety, sorrow, and pain.	Agree	Disagree
18. I am a "people person."	Agree	Disagree
19. I prefer to be alone.	Agree	Disagree

How to Manage and Avoid In-Session Violence and Threats

It is an invaluable reminder that we are working with individuals who are mentally ill and that this can pose serious risks. Working with individuals along the antisocial spectrum increases the risk of being the target of several types of crime, including stalking and assault. This exercise is designed to assist you, the clinician, in maintaining control of the session and to help you be ever vigilant about how your client is responding internally and externally.

The following is a list of indicators that your client may be having difficulty with session content.

Client Indicators
• Client has an increase in respiration and sweating
• Client begins to fidget (when this not usual)
• Speech tone may deepen or rise
• Speech rate may increase
• Increase in motor movement (e.g., hands shake or legs bounce)
• Client moves closer to the edge of his or her seat
• Client sits forward
• Client's eye contact drastically changes between fixation or avoidance
• Client attempts to avoid certain topics (that he or she is not prepared to address)
• Client displays loss of future orientation
• Client displays decompensating mental status
• Client displays deterioration of insight and judgment
• Client displays sexual fixation on you (the therapist)
• Client begins to discuss acts of violence in vague terms, but it appears relevant to you
• History of violent acts or intimidation toward perceived authority figures
• History of questionable medication compliance

This list is not all-inclusive. You know your client best, but it is critical to be aware of these issues and keep yourself safe. Managing in-session violence includes more than just monitoring your client's mental and physical state; it also includes the therapist taking steps to ensure his or her own safety.

Therapist Safety Procedures

- Sit closest to the door

- Alert other staff about possible client problems and have protocol in place if violence occurs

- Never see clients without other professionals or support staff present

- If after hours or on weekends, make sure you send texts or e-mails to other professionals or support staff at the start and end of session

- Be cognizant of and avoid intense power struggles

- Screen your clients and know their backgrounds

- Permit colleagues or support staff to walk in if there is yelling or loud or odd noises

- Be aware of pictures, drawings, or other personal items in your office (which can increase the likelihood of stalking)

- "Google" yourself and use other internet search engines to check the availability of your home address and personal information

- Monitor your Facebook®, Twitter®, LinkedIn® and other social media traffic for odd or unusual connections

---

When you have a client who begins to get upset, and you feel that he or she may act out in session, follow these steps:

1. Make a mental note of the content that appears to be upsetting the client.
2. Calmly and slowly remove all sharp or threatening objects from within the client's reach (e.g., pencils or pens).
3. Immediately move to more benign content.
4. *You can end the session here, but be aware that the client may go out and harm someone else.*
5. Maintain control of the session by using a soothing and slower tone. If the client models your behavior, he or she is deescalating.
6. Try not to look frightened. (Clients on the antisocial spectrum find this particularly encouraging.)
7. Suggest some relaxation techniques:
   a. Deep breathing
   b. Mindfulness
   c. Progressive muscle relaxation

8. If the client continues to be unabated in his or her frustration or intimidation, firmly state that you think the session should end for today, walk to the door (never turning your back on the client), and ask him or her to leave. *Be aware that he or she may go out and harm someone else, and consult your state rules and guidelines pertaining to Tarasoff.**

9. Make detailed notes about the session and consult a colleague about the incident, giving the client's name and other identifying information—this is not a breach of confidentiality, as your safety and the safety of others is in question.

10. If you see the client again, you can process the experience, but do so from a curious and cautious standpoint; for example, "You seemed to become very upset when I mentioned …" or "Tell me what it was like for you last session."

11. Be aware that no one thinks that in-session violence is going to happen to them until it does. One example is the murder of Kathryn Faughey, Ph.D., a psychologist who was stabbed to death in her office (Munsey, 2008).

---

*Tarasoff v. Regents of the University of California was a case in which the Supreme Court of California ruled that mental health professionals have a duty to protect individuals who are being threatened with bodily harm by a client. The professional may notify police, warn the intended victim, and/or take other reasonable steps to protect the threatened individual. See your state rules and guidelines pertaining to "duty to warn."

Secondary Gain/Assertiveness

Working with individuals on the antisocial spectrum brings about many challenges, including identifying the motivators for their behavior. It is important to always be aware of the primary and secondary motivators/gains that are at work.

Primary Gain
A benefit that involves the lessening of emotional conflict and release from anxiety or other uncomfortable experiences.

Secondary Gain
An indirect benefit gained by NOT solving the problem, typically through being ill or incapacitated. Such gains may include monetary and disability benefits, personal attention, or escape from unpleasant situations and responsibilities.

Identifying the motivators behind your client's behavior can prove useful in treatment. Many individuals on the antisocial spectrum utilize negative behaviors for some benefit or payoff because they do not know how or do not want to use more assertive and appropriate methods to get their needs met. For example, family members may be more selective in challenging the client on negative behaviors, thus allowing the person to do whatever he or she wants to do without pressure or confrontation. A key component in treatment is to assess the benefit associated with achieving the secondary gain.

Steinmetz and Tabenkin provide a list of the types of "difficult patients," but this list actually identifies secondary gain behaviors that any client, particularly clients along the antisocial spectrum, utilize to circuitously get their needs met.

Secondary Gain Behaviors
• Being violent, aggressive, verbally abusive • Having unresolved repeated complaints • Making multiple complaints—a "shopping list" • Having psychosomatic complaints • Complaining, never being satisfied • Being manipulative, lying • Saying "everything hurts" • Having a high anxiety level • Reporting "pain in the neck" • Being demanding, breaking boundaries, exploiting the therapist • Being angry at the doctor • Being uncooperative

Next Steps

Which of these behaviors fits your client on the antisocial spectrum? The Therapist Exercise—Steps to Decrease Secondary Gain Behaviors can help you identify the secondary gain behavior, its root, its reinforcer(s), and other critical factors that you will need to be aware of before you can lessen or extinguish them. As these behaviors are lessened or extinguished, clients can work on increasing assertive behaviors. Utilizing more assertive behavior not only helps your clients to lessen secondary gain behaviors and antisocial acting out but also allows them to develop better relationships, make more money through longer-term employment, and build trust with children, family, and valuable others.

The Goal Achievement Worksheet, which follows the Therapist Exercise, is designed to be given to your client to help him or her conceptualize secondary gain behavior(s) and learn assertiveness skills to better achieve his or her goals. Once your client has completed the worksheet, go over it in session and apply it directly to his or her choices to get his or her needs met. Use this worksheet regularly to encourage assertiveness.

Steps to Decrease Secondary Gain Behaviors

1. **What is the secondary gain to be achieved from identified behavior(s)?**

_____

_____

_____

_____

_____

2. **How does your client see his or her behavior as meeting his or her needs?**

_____

_____

_____

_____

_____

3. **Does this secondary gain behavior fit a historical theme for the client?**

_____

_____

_____

_____

_____

If it does, what has been the outcome?

_____

_____

_____

_____

4. **Will conducting an assessment assist in identifying secondary gain behaviors and outcomes (i.e., MMPI-2, MCMI-III, PAI)?**   Yes   No

5. **Does your client possess insight into his or her secondary gain behavior(s)?**   Yes   No
   a. If yes, this needs to be a central focus in treatment about behavior and consequences.
   b. If no, you need to gather evidence to support your therapeutic approach that secondary gain behaviors are insufficient for long-term goal attainment.

6. **What limits can you put in place to lessen or remove the significant benefit or payoff?**

   _____

   _____

   _____

   _____

   _____

   _____

7. **Would session management assist in decreasing secondary gain behaviors?**
   (This includes increasing or decreasing time intervals between sessions.)

   _____

   _____

   _____

   _____

   _____

   _____

8. **Would your client be receptive to assertiveness training to get his or her needs met?**

   a. If yes, see Goal Achievement Worksheet.
   b. If no, reevaluate the therapeutic approach and find a means to align with your client on how to "do things differently" to get his or her needs met. Sometimes the benefit or payoff is too significant or he or she is not ready.

   _____

   _____

   _____

   _____

Goal Achievement

Directions: Communicating assertively means clearly and calmly expressing what you want without being too passive or too aggressive. Learning to communicate assertively does not guarantee that you will have your needs met, but it makes it more likely, and it can improve your relationships with other people. Please answer the questions as honestly and completely as you can.

1. **What goal do you want to achieve?**

   _____

   _____

   _____

   _____

2. **What is the easy road to achieve your goal?** (This can include manipulation or other indirect means.)

   _____

   _____

   _____

   _____

3. **What is the hard road to achieve your goal?** (This includes direct and clear behavior.)

   _____

   _____

   _____

   _____

4. **What is it like when you are told "no" or do not get your anticipated outcome?**

   _____

   _____

   _____

   _____

5. **Circle which body language fits with your personal style to get your needs met:**

a. Face the other person, standing or sitting straight.
b. Listen carefully to what her or she says.
c. Have a pleasant facial expression.
d. Keep your voice calm and pleasant.
e. Make sure that your body language supports what you are saying (e.g., do not make the mistake of nodding your head when you are trying to say "no").

6. **Circle which communication technique fits with your personal style to get your needs met:**

a. Work out beforehand what you want to say and rehearse it.
b. Repeat your reply, using exactly the same words, over and over again and stick to what you have decided.
c. Keep repeating your point, using a calm and pleasant voice.
d. Not being put off by clever arguments or by what the other person says.
e. Not being pulled into an argument or having to explain your decision.

7. **Are you willing to compromise on your goal?**   Yes   No

a. If yes, what part?

_____

_____

_____

_____

b. If no, it is important to recognize that few goals are achieved 100% of the time.

8. **How else can you achieve your goal using a more assertive method?**

_____

_____

_____

_____

Can They Collaborate?

If you have worked with individuals along the antisocial spectrum for any period of time, you have come to understand that manipulation is part of the process. However, it is essential that the client is able to work collaboratively with you (the therapist) toward the goal of improved psychological well-being in order to achieve therapeutic success. The Collaboration Checklist that follows helps you to determine whether your client is able to do this.

Individuals who fall into the high or extreme range of the antisocial spectrum are least likely to benefit from psychological treatment (Hare, 1998; Hare et al., 2000), and the inability to collaborate is one of the primary reasons for this.

The majority of the questions in the checklist are designed to identity factors that support your client being able to participate in treatment and reap a benefit. However, there are certain questions, identified by an asterisk, that indicate a significantly higher probability that the individual is *not* able to collaborate in treatment due to being farther along on the antisocial spectrum. Those individuals within the severe ASPD category, which includes sociopaths and psychopaths, are unlikely to benefit from traditional insight-oriented treatment, due to a lack of ability to collaborate honestly with the therapist.

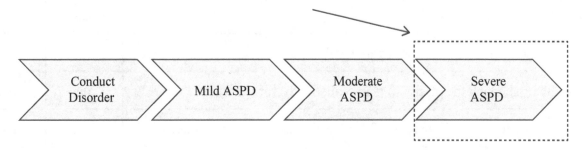

Next Steps

The Collaboration Checklist is a dimensional measure, meaning that the more positive factors you identify, the higher the probability that your client can collaborate during the course of treatment. You will reverse score those questions identified with an asterisk (*); in other words, you will give 1 point to those questions answered "no". For example, question 4 "Does he or she have a history of using cruelty to gain power?*" If you marked "Yes" for this question, you would not give a point; if you marked "No" you would give a point. Use the information gathered from the checklist to build on the positive factors to connect with your client in treatment.

Collaboration

Directions: Think of a particular client and answer the following questions about his or her ability to collaborate with you and participate in treatment.

1. Is he or she motivated for change?	Yes	No
2. Does he or she see value in psychological improvement?	Yes	No
3. Can he or she see your perspective on getting better?	Yes	No
4. Does he or she have a history of using cruelty to gain power?*	Yes	No
5. Does he or she have a clear purpose or reason to get better (e.g., staying out of jail, improved relationship with child)?	Yes	No
6. Does he or she trust you?	Yes	No
7. Is he or she devoid of guilt for negative behaviors?*	Yes	No
8. Does he or she lack the ability to plan realistically for the future?*	Yes	No
9. Does he or she take responsibility for gains and failures in treatment?	Yes	No
10. Does he or she lack empathy?*	Yes	No
11. Does he or she take responsibility for his or her own behavior and outcomes?	Yes	No
12. Does he or she need control at all times, inside and outside of session?*	Yes	No
13. Does he or she see you as someone with the skill to help him or her?	Yes	No
14. Does he or she disrespect others' boundaries?*	Yes	No
15. Do you have a positive therapeutic relationship with him or her?	Yes	No
16. Does he or she understand his or her own emotions?	Yes	No
17. Is he or she superficially charming?*	Yes	No
18. Can he or she control his or her own emotions?	Yes	No
19. Does he or she have a history of emotional manipulation?*	Yes	No
20. Does he or she lack genuine emotional reactions, other than anger?*	Yes	No

The "Wrong-Patient Syndrome"

Benjamin stated that "'The Wrong-Patient Syndrome' cannot be treated," meaning that participants wishing to benefit from treatment must be willing to see their impact on their environment and those within it. They cannot hold the view that they are simply pawns that are unable to combat the wills of the environment on their life. These clients must be willing to take responsibility for their life and behaviors. One of the most challenging areas when working with individuals along the antisocial spectrum is helping them to recognize and take responsibility for their actions. This is a critical component when working with these individuals, because when they are ready to take responsibility, they are also ready to take healthy control over their lives.

Next Steps

The sentence stems in the Taking Control Worksheet that follows helps address responsibility in key aspects of your client's life.

The worksheet is broken up into two parts, which can be given together or separately. The first part is designed to give the therapist an idea of the client's readiness to take responsibility. It examines the client's viewpoint on power, control, and choice, as well as the willingness and efficacy he or she believes he or she has over his or her life. A key component of personality disorders is an external locus of control (the belief that events in life are beyond one's control and due to external forces). Once your client has completed Part I, go over the responses and look for a theme that indicates an external locus of control. Is it pervasive across contexts or is it only limited to home, work, or relationships? Does it pertain to one particular person, such as mother, father, or spouse, or extend across all people in the client's life?

Part II provides a sense of the client's responsibility and willingness to take control of his or her environment. It examines your client's internal locus of control (the belief that events in life are within one's control and related to the choices one makes). Part II indicates potential areas of control and areas in which your client sees himself or herself as valuable and efficacious in a positive and thoughtful manner. However, those further along on the antisocial spectrum are likely to see Part II as an opportunity to illuminate aspects of their life in which they have dominance and power; this may indicate that your client is not ready for the responsibility of healthy interaction and the "give-and-take" that is involved in positive relationships. As therapists working with clients on the antisocial spectrum know, this material can give a view of how entrenched the antisocial/deviant view actually is; this provides valuable clinical information about readiness for change and growth through treatment.

Taking Control Part I

Directions: Please complete the sentences below. Answer each to the best of your ability without editing your responses.

I have no control over _____

_____

_____

I have no choice about _____

_____

_____

I feel powerless over _____

_____

_____

There is nothing I can do about _____

_____

_____

It is up to _____ **to make things different.**

I cannot do better because _____

_____

_____

I cannot stop (behavior) _____ **because** _____

_____

_____

I am unlucky because _____

_____

_____

Taking Control Part II

Directions: Please complete the sentences below. Answer each to the best of your ability without editing your responses.

I can control _____

_____

_____

I can choose to _____

_____

_____

I have power over _____

_____

_____

I can do something about _____

_____

_____

It is up to _____ to make things different

I can do it differently because _____

_____

_____

I can stop (behavior) _____ because _____

_____

_____

I am fortunate because _____

_____

_____

Can You Bond With a Client on the Antisocial Personality Disorder Spectrum?

The further along the antisocial spectrum your client is, the harder it will be to develop rapport and a therapeutic bond. The following chart lists the four necessary foundational factors that enable a therapeutic collaboration to occur. The description of each and how it pertains to treatment will be discussed as well.

Facilitating Communication
Assisting With Problem Solving
Helping Explore Negative Behaviors
Encouraging Positive Self-Care and Independence

Facilitating Communication entails the ability to bring about negative thoughts and feelings in a safe therapeutic environment for you and your client. The client on the antisocial spectrum, depending on how far along he or she is, is likely to have difficulty with self-control and managing adverse and negative emotional states. If your client is able to manage his or her emotions and assist in two-way communication, a critical factor of the therapeutic relationship is present.

Assisting With Problem Solving includes your client's ability and willingness to honestly explore his or her involvement in the problem(s) in his or her life and take suggestions to make changes. The client on the antisocial spectrum is often expecting advice (leaving the responsibility on the therapist) to solve his or her problem(s) and is not interested in assisting with solutions. If your client is able to work with you to find genuine and viable solutions, a critical factor of the therapeutic relationship is present.

Helping Explore Negative Behaviors entails your client's ability and willingness to examine the impact of his or her behavior(s) and test new prosocial behaviors. The technique of immediacy is often helpful in determining if this factor is present, as this brings to the forefront the client's ability to see the impact his or her behavior has on you (the therapist). For example, your client becomes angry and starts yelling in session. Immediacy would include professionally telling your client how you feel about him or her yelling in session. You would then explore other, more prosocial means, to express himself or herself. If your client is able to examine negative behaviors and test new healthy ones, a critical factor of the therapeutic relationship is present.

Encouraging Positive Self-Care and Independence includes your client taking suggestions made in session and testing them out within his or her life. This indicates that your client is motivated to change. However, the client on the antisocial spectrum often does a poor job of self-care and is typically dependent on substances, gang involvement, how he or she is viewed by others, the need for power and control, and many other aspects that impugn his or her sense of true independence. When you see that your client is moving outside of this dependency and more toward positive self-care, it indicates that a critical factor of the therapeutic relationship is present.

In addition to these four foundational factors for therapeutic collaboration, the chart that follows shows additional necessary aspects to consider. These factors relate to the ability and commitment of your client to change and remain in treatment when it becomes difficult. These factors also take into account the client's ability to use resources in his or her environment to promote prosocial change and a healthier lifestyle.

Additional Foundational Factors for Therapeutic Collaboration

- Ability to discuss and achieve common understanding

- Ability to provide honest information related to past and present behaviors

- Ability to create base for therapeutic support

- Ability to avoid engaging in serial therapy (moving to a different therapist when treatment becomes difficult)

- Ability to complete simple and complex tasks, inside and outside of session

- Ability to share resources to address common issues

- Ability to merge resources to create new and positive opportunities

- Ability to share ideas and be willing to pull resources from existing systems

- Ability to develop commitment to treatment

- Ability to develop a shared vision and achieve therapeutic short-term and long-term goals

- Ability to build interdependent system to address issues and opportunities

---

Transference and Countertransference

When working with clients with personality disorders you are certain to have transference and/or countertransference reactions. This is associated with the client's tendency to read others and their strengths and weakness to determine if they are "safe," or in the case of the client on the antisocial spectrum, if they are "prey." This tendency is typically developed over many years and functions as an adaptive skill for the client.

Freud defined *transference* as thoughts, feelings, conflicts, and/or needs that are displaced onto the therapist in a manner that mimics dynamics with important others from the client's life. This is a natural byproduct of therapy. As the therapeutic relationship grows, the therapist becomes an attachment object that the client begins to see and interact with as a valuable other in his or her life. In many cases, this "other" is someone such as the client's mother, father, or spouse. This is a good thing, and it means that a relationship has developed. However, when working with an individual along the antisocial spectrum, this attachment is difficult to develop, and genuine transference is uncommon.

> **Transference can be managed by clarifying roles
> of the *client* and *therapist* and of the *relationship***

Those who approach therapy from an analytic framework are prepared for transference and work with it; however, those who do not work from this orientation attempt to understand and manage transference by clarifying roles, defining what treatment means, and examining the rules and goals of treatment. For example, a client becomes angry with you for making his or her life more difficult and making him or her pay money for seeing you. The therapist is now being seen as a threatening object to the client, and this requires clarification of reality. The clarification is meant to restore reality to the role of the therapist and the true purpose of the therapeutic work and relationship.

> **Managing transference is a constant with the difficult client
> who prefers to repeat the past instead of changing it**

On the other side of this therapeutic coin is countertransference, which is very common when working with clients who have personality disorders. *Countertransference* is when the therapist's unconscious and defensive reactions are projected onto the client; it causes a very visceral reaction in most therapists. Freud theorized that countertransference is a result of the therapist's failure to resolve his or her own personal issues and conflicts, and it hampers the therapists' ability to fully understand his or her clients. The client on the antisocial spectrum is likely to use this imbalance for his or her own benefit, which can include financial, sexual, or other manipulative ends.

Next Steps

The Countertransference Scale, which follows, is designed to help you, the therapist, identify countertransference reactions, as these typically go unnoticed by many therapists and may manifest as adverse emotional reactions to therapeutic content. You can focus on a specific client or all your clients in general. This scale is also beneficial to give to supervisees to get a sense of the risk of countertransference and can open the door to some necessary and critical supervision discussions. **A scoring table is provided in Appendix A.**

After you have filled out and scored the scale, see the Managing Countertransference section immediately following to help you address this issue in yourself as a therapist or in your supervisee as a supervisor.

Countertransference Scale

Directions: Please answer each question as honestly as you can. Remember, the purpose of this form is for you and possibly your supervisor or colleague to gain a better understanding how you see yourself when working with intensely emotional clients. A scoring table can be found in Appendix A.

1. I have a firm sense of my therapeutic identity.	Yes	No
2. I am able to tell the difference between my feelings and those elicited from me by my client.	Yes	No
3. I am aware of my personal issues and cognizant to not bring them into therapy.	Yes	No
4. I often use my own experience to connect with my clients.	Yes	No
5. I am unable to distance myself from my client's issues.	Yes	No
6. I am able to emotionally separate from my clients to gain better perspective.	Yes	No
7. I am able to see my clients' emotional reactions as indicators of their past issues.	Yes	No
8. I am unable to leave my personal issues outside of therapy.	Yes	No
9. I am aware of the personal impact I have on my clients.	Yes	No
10. I try to emotionally connect to my client when he or she talks about material that is uncomfortable for me.	Yes	No
11. I am unable to distinguish between my client's needs and my own.	Yes	No
12. I have trouble remaining objective when my clients have intense emotional reactions.	Yes	No
13. I am comfortable when my client presents strong feelings in session.	Yes	No
14. I am unaware of what motivates my behavior with my clients.	Yes	No
15. I attempt to disengage emotionally during session when my anxiety is linked with my client's emotions.	Yes	No
16. I am able to remain aware of what motivates the emotions in my client, even during times of intense emotional expression by him or her.	Yes	No
17. I try to be liked by my clients.	Yes	No
18. It is hard for me to be professionally and not personally connected to my clients.	Yes	No
19. I am comfortable providing intense feedback to my clients, even when I know it may upset them.	Yes	No
20. I tend to overempathize with my clients.	Yes	No

Managing Countertransference

Those who score in the "fair" or "poor" range on the Countertransference Scale are at a high risk of having issues with countertransference. This becomes a particular issue when working with clients on the antisocial spectrum. Those who score in the "fair" or "poor" range should consider addressing their emotional concerns and how they connect with and relate to their clients.

> **Always know the root of your emotional trigger(s) when in and out of session**

If this is a continual issue, the therapist should consider entering therapy himself or herself or, at minimum, be willing to address this issue in consultation.

> **There is *confidentiality*, but there are NO SECRETS in therapy**

The concept of confidentiality and NO SECRETS in treatment means that therapists are entrusted to keep information confidential and honor their clients' information and life experiences. However, at no time are we to keep secrets. Secrets include things like holding hands, kissing, or exchanging personal photos with your client, and other inappropriate behaviors inside or outside of the session and keeping this information private. If these things sound shocking to you, they should. When you harbor secrets, you risk losing your license and more in some cases. When you work with the client on the antisocial spectrum and become caught up in transference and countertransference issues, the probability of developing secrets increases significantly.

If you feel yourself becoming emotional toward a client (the most common reactions being anger, disgust, fear, and attraction—having a "crush"), ask yourself, "What is it about this client that is causing me to feel this way?"

If you are having trouble cognitively reorienting when triggered, engage in **self-soothing techniques** to emotionally stabilize yourself. You do not need to stop treatment to do this. Here are some tips:

1. Focus on your breathing and assess where you are emotionally.
2. Think about something unrelated to the emotional moment to pull yourself out of it, and then reengage from a more stable emotional standpoint.
3. Take note of what you smell in your office: a candle, air freshener, etc.?
4. Grab a mint! Have mints within reach and focus on the taste and feel within your mouth.
5. What do you hear, other than your client's voice?

The key is to:

> **Step outside of the emotional moment and reorient yourself**

Remember, transference and countertransference are phenomena that are likely to occur in every therapeutic relationship, and this likelihood is even greater when working with difficult clients, including clients on the antisocial spectrum.

Part Three
Narcissistic Personality Disorder Spectrum

Narcissistic Personality Disorder and Its Subtypes

Narcissistic personality disorder (NPD) is composed of "grandiosity, need for admiration, and lack of empathy" (APA, 2013, p. 645). It seems that narcissism is becoming the norm within United States culture, but Stinson and colleagues (2008) found a lifetime prevalence rate of NPD in 6.2% of Americans. A gender breakdown showed that 7.7% of Americans with NPD were male and 4.8% were female. Though it is a relatively uncommon disorder, NPD development is complex and clients on the narcissistic spectrum present unique challenges within a treatment setting. The following components make up the narcissistic spectrum:

Self-Confidence is an adaptive characteristic to possess and one that each of us hopes to have. It can be defined as the belief in one's abilities pertaining to who one is and the decisions one makes. As therapists, we are often attempting to build this in our clients. Self-confidence is based in reality and should represent a balance between skills the individual can perform well and those he or she cannot.

When healthy self-confidence grows into a pathological construct, the preoccupation with managing one's impression of confidence starts to lay the foundation for NPD. When success becomes more important than self-respect or self-confidence and the individual's culture overvalues image, it fosters a sense of narcissistic fragility, which promotes the individual to the next stage along the narcissistic spectrum (Lowen, 1985).

Self-Preoccupation grows out of self-confidence as the excessive interest in the self grows and the view of others and the world becomes nebulous and of lesser value. The preoccupation with the self begins to adversely impact others at this point along the spectrum. Other people may begin to self-select out of the preoccupied individual's life, as relationships, romantic or platonic, appear one-sided. Employment may begin to suffer as self-preoccupation causes the individual to feel that he or she is entitled to certain treatment. For example, a self-preoccupied individual who works as a waitress feels that she should work every Friday and Saturday night without having to work Tuesdays and Wednesdays (the slowest nights). This causes her to quit and rail against management, whom she believes mistreats her. She is only preoccupied with herself and her needs and not those of her employer or the other servers with whom she works.

In some cases, the self-preoccupied individual may enter treatment. Such a client often exhibits resistance to learning empathy and a deterioration of social skills, as the value he or she places on the self is too significant. Over time and through the loss of friends and financial stability due to serial unemployment, the individual may become willing to see the benefit of doing things differently, and he or she may become an active participant in treatment. However, if he or she does not and his or her reality testing becomes more clouded, he or she moves toward self-absorption.

Self-Absorption is a component that if not reined in, either through therapy or severe life experiences, will continue to exacerbate into NPD. The person's ability to empathize is significantly impaired, and the focus on his or her own emotions, interests, and situations intensifies and becomes so great that these same components become irrelevant when expressed in others. The absorbed individual may offend others and not take notice or feel frustrated and confused when "called out" on his or her behavior. His or her behavior is often upsetting to others, and he or she is oblivious to its impact.

The self-absorbed individual is less likely than the self-preoccupied individual to come into treatment. This is due to the feeling that one's interpersonal conflicts arise due to others' problems and not one's own. Additionally, this type of client typically believes that others should adjust their views and approaches to fit his or her needs and expectations. He or she has few friends and tends to easily attain and lose jobs or careers; employment tends to be short-lived.

The self-absorbed individual has not reached NPD just yet. He or she still values the opinions of others, though much less than those at the previous two levels along the spectrum, and does not show it in a healthy manner. A self-absorbed individual tends to engage socially with the intent to come off as interesting, charming, clever, attractive, or special. He or she tends to be socially impaired due to having little to no interest in what other individuals are thinking and feeling, as he or she spends too much time talking about himself or herself. As self-absorption begins to grow and adversely impact the world around him or her, narcissism develops to pathological levels and begins to reinforce itself until he or she attains NPD.

Narcissistic Personality Disorder is an extreme form of self-absorption. Like all personality disorders, the pathology is designed to reinforce itself so that the world of the individual with NPD justifies his or her beliefs and behaviors. The criteria are:

- **Experiences extreme self-importance**
- **Fantasies of power**
- **Has a sense of entitlement**
- **Requires admiration**
- **Lacks empathy**
- **Sees self as unique**
- **Is interpersonally exploitive**
- **Has vulnerable self-esteem**
- **Becomes enraged if disagreed with**
- **Has low vocational functioning**

Narcissistic personality disorder is a complex, but not impossible, disorder to treat. The worksheets in this section address critical therapist and client factors to attenuate narcissistic components and the individuals they impact.

Narcissistic Personality Spectrum

The narcissistic personality spectrum is composed of self-confidence, self-preoccupation, self-absorption, and narcissistic personality disorder. It is critical when working with an individual who falls along this spectrum to identify where he or she is to accurately tailor interventions.

Next Steps

The Self and Other Worksheet is to be given to your client to complete and for you to score and to discuss in session. Many of the responses to each pair of questions provide valuable information when working with the client on the narcissistic spectrum.

These responses can help you, the therapist, determine how self-focused your client is, as well as the value he or she places on others within his or her interpersonal world (e.g., friends, family, bosses, co-workers). **Scoring for the worksheet can be found in Appendix A.**

The exercises within the NPD spectrum section of this workbook can be used with any client to thwart or lessen advancement along the narcissistic spectrum. For example, using empathy exercises with the self-preoccupied client is a viable and useful intervention, as it increases the awareness and emotional value of those around him or her.

Self and Other

Directions: Below are two similar statements that relate to you and those around you. Mark (✓) the statement that most identifies your belief or view. If you identify with both statements, place a (✓) in front of the one you think is most important.

1.	a. _____	I have a sense of physical well-being.
	b._____	I lack a sense of physical well-being.
2.	a._____	I am valued by others.
	b._____	I do not have value to others.
3.	a._____	I am attractive to others.
	b._____	Other people do not find me attractive.
4.	a._____	I am healthy.
	b._____	I have health problems.
5.	a._____	I tend to follow the rules.
	b._____	I secretly enjoy breaking rules.
6.	a._____	I can easily say "I'm sorry."
	b._____	It is hard for me to say "I'm sorry."
7.	a._____	I am aware of my feelings.
	b._____	I have trouble knowing how I feel.
8.	a._____	My feelings should come first.
	b._____	My feelings are not that important.
9.	a._____	I spend an average amount of time looking in the mirror.
	b._____	I spend an above-average amount of time looking in the mirror.
10.	a._____	I get satisfaction from listening to others.
	b._____	It is hard to listen to others complain.
11.	a._____	I value what I feel over what others feel.
	b._____	My feelings have the same value as everyone else's.
12.	a._____	I often wonder how my friends/family members are feeling.
	b._____	I rarely concern myself with how my friends/family are feeling.
13.	a._____	It is hard for me to identify when a friend/family member is upset.
	b._____	I can tell when a friend/family member is upset.

14.	a._____	I often go over/rehearse how I was perceived in social situations.
	b._____	I am not too concerned with how I am perceived in social situations.
15.	a._____	I value my boss/co-worker's opinion.
	b._____	My boss/co-worker's opinion has little value.
16.	a._____	I am a modest person.
	b._____	Modesty does not concern me.
17.	a._____	I am good because everyone tells me so.
	b._____	I get embarrassed when people compliment me.
18.	a._____	I am a special person.
	b._____	I am no better or worse than most people.
19.	a._____	I tend to make great decisions.
	b._____	I am not a good decision maker.
20.	a._____	I am concerned with other people's feelings.
	b._____	Other people's feelings are of no concern to me.

Harm to Self and Other

Individuals with narcissistic traits and NPD are at a significantly low risk to complete suicide, but under certain circumstances are likely to commit homicide. However, either suicide or homicide can occur when the narcissistic individual incurs a narcissistic injury, which can be defined as a perceived threat to one's self-esteem and/or self-worth. Two seminal studies conducted by Gilligan and Lion explored the acts of violence to self or other that may result from narcissistic injury and rage. Narcissistic rage entails a wide variety of responses that can range from being aloof to acting violently. In both studies, it was found that when an individual with narcissistic traits or NPD is injured in such a way that he or she sees himself or herself as ineffective and devalues the self, he or she is at a higher risk of harm to self and/or others. In these cases, an assessment of narcissism and threat to self and others should be conducted. This questionnaire is a tool to assist the therapist in determining if a narcissistic injury has occurred and if the client is experiencing thoughts about harming himself or herself or another person.

Next Steps

The Harm to Self or Other Worksheet, which follows, should never supplant clinical intervention or judgment or the need to intervene in cases in which you deem your client a threat to self or other. It is not designed to be a stand-alone tool to determine narcissism or narcissistic threat to self or other. If you believe the client may be a danger to self or other, contact your local emergency room or law enforcement and follow recommended guidelines per your state's licensing board.

The Harm to Self or Other Worksheet is to be given to your client early in the session, either to fill out on his or her own or with the therapist. It should be reviewed prior to the client leaving the session for the day. **Scoring can be found in Appendix A.**

Harm to Self and Other

Directions: Please indicate Yes or No for each question. Your therapist will calculate the answers and derive related scores. Please answer as honestly and truthfully as you can.

1. I used to believe I was better than others.	Yes	No
2. I have told someone I was going to kill myself.	Yes	No
3. I feel hurt about what someone said to me.	Yes	No
4. I have had a plan to kill myself in the past.	Yes	No
5. I question my ability to achieve great things.	Yes	No
6. I think someone should pay for hurting me.	Yes	No
7. I can see why people do not admire me.	Yes	No
8. I am thinking about killing myself.	Yes	No
9. I understand why people question my abilities.	Yes	No
10. Someone should pay for making me feel this way.	Yes	No
11. There is a very likely chance I will end my life someday.	Yes	No
12. I am finding it hard not to act out toward the person who has offended/hurt me.	Yes	No
13. I no longer think I am better than anyone else.	Yes	No
14. I often fantasize about hurting the person who hurt me.	Yes	No

Building Mastery

It may seem surprising to see a worksheet for boosting self-confidence within the recommended treatments for clients along the NPD spectrum, but many of the characteristics of narcissism are derived from poor self-confidence and poor mastery. The Building Mastery Worksheet is designed to help identify areas of strength and build mastery, with the intent of reducing the client's narcissistic beliefs and behaviors as self-confidence and mastery are enhanced. It may be difficult for a client on the narcissistic spectrum to complete this worksheet honestly due to high levels of narcissism that may shield him or her from true introspection. The client is likely to have difficulty identifying areas for skills enhancement in order to build mastery, because, the person's level of narcissism makes him or her feel falsely complete in his or her skillset.

However, as the individual moves along the narcissistic spectrum, his or her development of skills and mastery lessens due to the individual's tendency to avoid receiving negative feedback or criticism, which functions to protect his or her fragile ego state and allow the individual to remain in his or her "comfort zone." *Without risk there is no growth* is a central therapeutic theme for the individual along the narcissistic spectrum. The therapist is advised to present this worksheet as an identified skill or high skill areas worksheet to encourage genuine participation.

Next Steps

The Building Mastery Worksheet will not be an easy task for the client on the narcissistic spectrum because he or she has potentially few areas of mastery, a reluctance to identify areas that are not perfect, and difficulty identifying areas in which he or she could improve. The therapist may need to guide the client to begin the worksheet and discuss how the client may benefit from building mastery. Once the worksheet is completed, use the information gathered to implement these components into your client's life to help him or her achieve mastery and lessen narcissistic defenses.

Building Mastery

Directions: Identify two areas where you want to increase your sense of mastery. Then, identify the mastery building blocks that will help you achieve each goal. There is a table of common building blocks that help people achieve mastery in their lives below. You can use each building block more than once. Lastly, describe how you will use these building blocks to build mastery and enhance your success. Your therapist may be a good resource to help complete and utilize this worksheet and the relevant information.

For example:

Master area A : _Be a better parent_

I can implement (add mastery building blocks from the table on page 71)

Think positively, engage in positive actions, be prepared, and act patiently

_____

_____

by (write _how_ you will use these building blocks to achieve mastery in area A)

Think about my children in positive ways, focus on what they do well, outwardly encourage them

when they struggle, create a schedule for them and me (allowing for flexibility), and stop and think

about the best reaction under times of stress

_____

_____

_____

Mastery area A _____

I can implement (add mastery building blocks from the table on page 71)

_____

_____

_____

by (write _how_ you will use these building blocks to achieve mastery in area B)

_____

_____

_____

Mastery area B _____

I can implement (add mastery building blocks from the table below)

_____

_____

_____

by (write *how* you will use these building blocks to achieve mastery in area C)

_____

_____

_____

• Think positively	• Change a small habit	• Finish what you start
• Pay attention to grooming	• Increase competence	• Face your fears
• Speak slowly	• Show gratitude	• Exercise restraint
• Engage in self-exploration	• Exercise	• Control anger
• Reduce negative thoughts	• Empower yourself	• Act patiently
• Engage in positive actions	• Get active	• Prioritize needs, not wants
• Be kind	• Work on small things	• Be willing to modify goals
• Be generous	• Develop clear goals	• Do not give up
• Be prepared	• Make deliberate decisions	• Maintain your healthy integrity
• Know your boundaries	• Give up addictions	• Identify roots of emotions

Attachment and the Narcissistic Spectrum

There are two types of narcissism that will be considered for the Viewpoint Worksheets 1 and 2, grandiose, or overt, and vulnerable, or covert, narcissism. These two types of narcissism share some components but can be distinguished by several factors (Wink, 1991), as shown in the following charts:

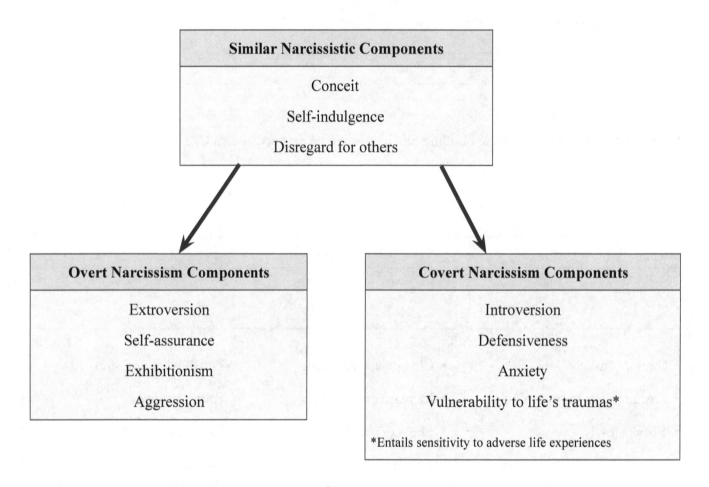

Similar Narcissistic Components

Conceit

Self-indulgence

Disregard for others

Overt Narcissism Components

Extroversion

Self-assurance

Exhibitionism

Aggression

Covert Narcissism Components

Introversion

Defensiveness

Anxiety

Vulnerability to life's traumas*

*Entails sensitivity to adverse life experiences

Individuals who meet criteria for the grandiose or overt type of narcissism tend to be classified as having a more dismissing attachment style, a stance of positive self-appraisal, and a denial of interpersonal distress. The vulnerable or covert narcissistic style tends to be represented by having a fearful or preoccupied attachment style, which indicates a negative self-appraisal that causes him or her not to say positive things about the self, experience interpersonal distress, and have a tendency to avoid relationships (Dickinson & Pincus, 2003).

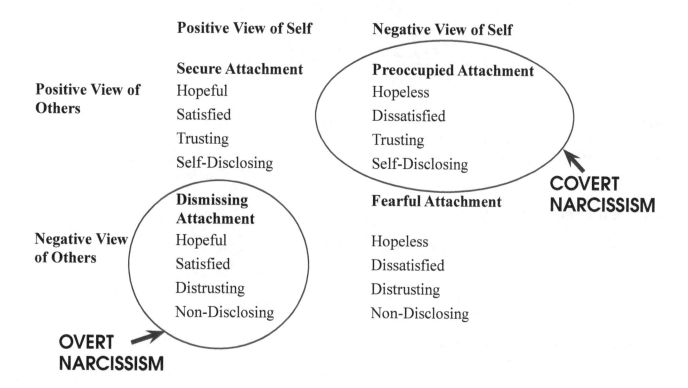

	Positive View of Self	Negative View of Self
Positive View of Others	**Secure Attachment** Hopeful Satisfied Trusting Self-Disclosing	**Preoccupied Attachment** Hopeless Dissatisfied Trusting Self-Disclosing
Negative View of Others	**Dismissing Attachment** Hopeful Satisfied Distrusting Non-Disclosing	**Fearful Attachment** Hopeless Dissatisfied Distrusting Non-Disclosing

COVERT NARCISSISM

OVERT NARCISSISM

Working with attachment issues with clients along the narcissistic spectrum brings about many complex issues and is one of the main reasons working with this population is so challenging. Bonding is exceptionally difficult for individuals along this spectrum because of their resistance to attach to the therapist and their utilization of ego-protective methods to get their needs met. The therapist must be aware that an asymmetrical relationship will exist in which the attachment figure (the therapist) supplies the environment for secure attachment to develop, rather than this security occurring in a more routine fashion over time. This imbalance will cause the therapist to feel that he or she is working harder trying to engage the client compared to other, non-narcissistic spectrum clients. It is not uncommon for narcissistic clients to seek constant adulation and praise through storytelling and fantasy, which can derail treatment if not controlled early in the process.

Next Steps

The following worksheets will help to address these core issues, but these are difficult areas for clients on the narcissistic spectrum. The further along the spectrum the client is, the more complicated the process becomes, because the focus of treatment shifts to the complex core issues of the client's attachment style (e.g., dismissing for the client with overt narcissism, preoccupied for the client with covert narcissism).

Two Viewpoint Worksheets are provided, one for the overt narcissism client (1) and one for the covert narcissism client (2). These worksheets are most effective when you have established a relationship that is honest with minimal ego resistance to growth and change. Ask your client to fill out the worksheet, and then discuss the answers in a very open and non-threatening manner. The client will be highly sensitive to feedback if he or has answered honestly. Remember, every answer is a valuable one. If your client gives an answer that you know is false, that still provides useful data in treatment. All information, even a lie, is fodder for treatment. In these cases, your client's answers can be seen as a projective.

Viewpoint [1]

Directions: Write your immediate thought after each sentence stem. *Do not edit your thoughts.* For example, the first sentence stem asks about how you judge people for a particular trait, and the second asks about what would help you change that immediate thought, if negative, or what would make it stronger, if positive.

People are trustworthy when:

_____

_____

_____

People can show they are trustworthy by:

_____

_____

The best way to connect with someone else is:

_____

_____

_____

You know you have connected to someone by:

_____

_____

People care when:

_____

_____

_____

You show someone you care by:

_____

_____

_____

People show how they value themselves by:

_____

_____

_____

You show how you value yourself when:

_____

_____

_____

Feedback is helpful when:

_____

_____

_____

You provide helpful feedback by:

_____

_____

_____

Being in the spotlight is important when:

_____

_____

_____

It is unimportant to be in the spotlight when:

_____

_____

_____

You defend yourself when:

_____

_____

_____

I do not feel I have to defend myself when:

_____

_____

_____

Viewpoint ²

Directions: Write your immediate thought after each sentence stem. *Do not edit your thoughts.* For example, the first sentence stem asks about how you judge people for a particular trait, and the second asks about what would help you change that immediate thought, if negative, or what would make it stronger, if positive.

People are trustworthy when:

_____

_____

_____

_____

People can show they are trustworthy by:

_____

_____

_____

_____

You know you can connect with someone else when:

_____

_____

_____

_____

People show they are worthy of being connected to by:

_____

_____

_____

_____

People care when:

_____

_____

_____

_____

You show someone you care by:

_____

_____

_____

_____

You should protect yourself when:

_____

_____

_____

_____

The best way to protect yourself is by:

_____

_____

_____

_____

Life hurts most when:

_____

_____

_____

_____

You avoid pain in life by:

_____

_____

_____

_____

Perfection Versus Excellence

There is a healthy drive for excellence that can be utilized in treatment to motivate clients to strive for a better life and build adaptive strategies. However, when striving for excellence is not done in moderation, it can hamper success and create serious issues for your clients. This continuum ranges from excellence to perfectionism and is an underlying core factor of narcissism at higher levels, as depicted here:

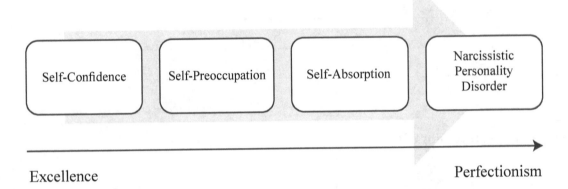

Excellence   Perfectionism

Perfection is the inability to accept anything that does not meet one's absolute standards. This sounds pathological and may make you think, "How could any aspect of this ever be adaptive?" At the other end of the spectrum, excellence is the drive to achieve something outstanding, without error. The existence of both excellence and perfectionism in your client indicates a need for control and a drive to understand his or her surroundings. The problem arises when he or she becomes so preoccupied, absorbed, or narcissistic that the perfection becomes an unwavering standard across all environments and interpersonal relationships. Using the drive to achieve excellence in treatment can help propel your clients forward, because they have internal motivation, a good thing. The costs and benefits of pursuing perfection must be weighed, and the motivation behind the striving for excellence should be explored before it reaches a pathological level that impairs growth and development.

Next Steps

The Pursuit of Excellence Worksheet is designed to help your client identify the costs and benefits of striving for excellence and the impact this may have on his or her life.

Pursuit of Excellence

Directions: In the following exercise, identify factors related to your pursuit of excellence, the motivating factors, and the costs and benefits. You will also be asked about how you can augment the advantages and lessen the disadvantages of striving for excellence. If you are stuck at any point, ask your therapist for assistance.

How has the pursuit of excellence helped you?

_____

_____

_____

_____

_____

_____

How has the pursuit of excellence hindered you?

_____

_____

_____

_____

_____

_____

_____

Rank the following motivating factors for you in the pursuit of excellence from 1 to 14, with 1 being the greatest motivating factor and 14 being the least.

_____ Fear of failure		_____ Thinking I deserve the best	
_____ Dissatisfaction with my accomplishments		_____ To overcome another's deficits	
_____ Always needing to be in control		_____ To avoid problems	
_____ Needing recognition for my excellence		_____ To avoid negative feelings	
_____ Preventing people from thinking less of me		_____ To fight my sense of inferiority	
_____ Being physically attractive		_____ To show off my intelligence	
_____ Having order and organization		_____ To win	

What are the advantages of using the excellence factors listed ranked?

_____

_____

_____

_____

_____

_____

What are the disadvantages of using the excellence factors ranked previously?

_____

_____

_____

_____

_____

_____

_____

Circle which is more beneficial, the advantages or disadvantages of striving for excellence?

        Excellence Advantages   **Excellence Disadvantages**

What can you do to revise the disadvantages and build on the advantages?
(You may need the help of your therapist with this.)

_____

_____

_____

_____

_____

_____

_____

_____

Surmount the Power Struggle

Power struggles are inherent when working with clients along the narcissistic spectrum. In many cases, the therapist is attempting to get his or her point across about how narcissism alienates others and causes greater problems. Clients develop narcissistic views as protective and adaptive responses, and these can cause the therapist to be pulled into the pathology, which may result in a power struggle. The following exercise is designed to help the therapist gain control of the session and manage content more effectively.

The problem with the power struggle is that the therapist cannot win. If the therapist is able to prove his or her point to be superior, it builds resentment in the client, and he or she pulls back from treatment. Additionally, if the therapist is able to decimate the client's point, this may cause a narcissistic injury that can lead the client to harm self or other. The best way to manage power struggles, aside from not getting pulled into them, is to maintain self-control. By doing this, the therapist keeps the trajectory of treatment on course and focused on client welfare.

Power struggles often bring up transference and counter transference issues. *Transference* can be defined as thoughts, feelings, conflicts, and/or needs that are displaced onto the therapist in a manner that mimics dynamics with important others from the client's life. *Countertransference* is when the therapist's unconscious and defensive reactions are projected onto the client; this causes a visceral reaction in most therapists. This reaction is part of what causes therapists to be pulled into power struggles.

Below are the five most common therapist reactions when working with an individual along the narcissistic spectrum that cause power struggles to occur. The intensity tends to be correlated with how far along the client is on the spectrum.

Therapist Reactions
1. Anger
2. Frustration
3. Hurt
4. Disappointment
5. Upset about lack of progress

Self-Confidence   Self-Preoccupation   Self-Absorption   Narcissistic Personality Disorder

Mild   Extreme

The most important thing to remember is:

> ### Countertransference reactions are normal and expected

Managing the session includes managing your own actions and reactions. You want to self-monitor your feelings, the dialogue between you and the narcissistic spectrum client, and your body language and facial expressions. You may not play poker with cards, but you are playing it in therapy with these types of clients.

Below are eight options for you to try when you are pulled into a power struggle. Some may fit with your therapeutic modality; some may not. Use the ones that fit and perhaps try one or two that do not to expand your session management skills. Each of these skills can be practiced while in session or outside of it.

- **Avoid "Us and Them" Thinking:** This entails thinking that the client is so different from you and your other clients that he or she is impossible to work with. Your client is now in the outgroup, and whether consciously or unconsciously, he or she will be treated as such. Try and consider what factors you and your client have in common. You have an advanced degree and you worked hard to get where you are in life. Has your client worked hard? Is he or she driven to achieve like you but afraid of failure? What is the common ground? This is not easy, but it is an invaluable exercise.

- **Manage Your Emotions:** Your expertise is in emotional control and management, but that does not mean that you cannot be pulled into an interaction in which you lose sight of these skills. You are working with someone who has had a lifetime of using skills to manage interpersonal relationships by throwing people off balance with his or her own emotions. Slow down, take notice of your emotions, and ask yourself, "Has [client name] hit a personal trigger?" This is when knowing your own personal issues is critical. If you do not know your own triggers, your client on the narcissistic spectrum (as well as your other clients with personality disorders) does, and he or she will use that to tip the interaction in his or her favor. This is not malicious, but adaptive for the client. It is how he or she survives. If he or she has hit a trigger, now is the time to use the pull out or concrete skill discussed later in this section and explore this issue after session in supervision with a trusted colleague or enter therapy yourself to learn about the issue and control it. Read the skill "Know Your Triggers."

- **Self-Monitor:** When working with complex clients, like those along the narcissistic spectrum, having a solid skill like self-monitoring is invaluable. The foundation of successful self-monitoring is being aware of your emotions and behaviors. Easy, right? Not if you are in the middle of a power struggle. Try the following steps:

  1. The target is to reach a sense of calm and clear focus.
  2. What evidence is present to indicate your current emotions and behavioral reactions? (e.g., clenched teeth, making a fist, leaning forward, flushed face, increase in respiration and heart rate).
  3. Ask yourself, "When I get/do [insert emotions/behavior], do I become ___ (e.g., closed minded, aggressive, withdrawn, argumentative)?"

4. Get control of your breathing; focus on that while your client is engaged in the power struggle. (He or she will not notice, as he or she is enthralled in the power struggle.)
5. Mentally reorient yourself to the discussion and issue.
6. Re-engage with a sense of calm and clear focus.

- **Know Your Triggers:** It is imperative that you know your personal triggers if you are going to work with clients who have personality disorders. Such clients build up the skill to read others. Some use it for manipulation and some, for self-protection, but all of them have this skill to varying degrees. Your clients on the narcissistic spectrum are not exempt. Your triggers are excellent ways to pull you into power struggles, throw you off balance, and cause you to engage in behaviors or say things you would not normally do or say. In these instances, your client is likely to use this against you to show his or her superiority and your incompetence (in his or her opinion). Triggers typically come from your past life experiences. For example, you may have a picture in your office from a marathon in which you ran in your hometown. You are proud of this, and you came in third. Your narcissistic client is likely to mention how good it is that you ran the marathon, but too bad you could not win and "just came in third." Your reaction, if this is a trigger, tells your client volumes about you. Pictures in your office, the signature in your email, your website content and design are all indicators of personal information and values and can be potential triggers. Can you answer the following question?

  My triggers are _____

  If you are having trouble identifying them, seek supervision or consultation or participate in therapy to explore it. The benefits of knowing your triggers are invaluable, but the consequences of not knowing them can be detrimental.

- **Disengage:** This is a simple technique to gain control of the power struggle. This entails mentally extracting yourself from the power struggle and making a general probe or reflection. For example, "This really seems to upset you," or "You have very strong feelings about this." It is hard to continue the power struggle if you take the gas out of the tank.

- **Assess Gain:** Power struggles are typically an exercise for control. All therapists know that there are many dynamics at play when conducting therapy, especially with the client on the narcissistic spectrum. In my experience, I have never gained anything by either "winning" or "losing" a power struggle, but I have spoken to therapists who hold the idea that if they can win, this will "teach the client a lesson." I would be cautious in subscribing to this belief and would want to be certain that what you gain is both a long-term and a short-term benefit to the client. I have seen this belief as a form of countertransference and not an ingredient of lessening narcissistic expression. It is always a good idea to consult with a colleague or supervisor to objectively examine whether there is anything to gain from "winning" or "losing" a power struggle.

- **Pull Out:** Sometimes power struggles become so heated and extreme that the best option is to pull out. Therapeutic pull out entails recognition that the session has reached a point of impasse, emotions are too extreme, objectivity is compromised by both parties (therapist and client), and the session needs to end. However, you do not want to end the session with bitter anger or other intense emotions, which builds resentment. First, recognize that you and your client are at an impasse, objectively identify emotions in you and your client as you see them, utilize "I" messages to convey your feelings (relaxation techniques may also be good here), and generate a possible solution, noting that ending today's session is a viable option on which you both should agree. I would assign out-of-session exercises (I do not like the word *homework*) to allow your client to fully process what occurred in session. Try to end in agreement or postponement of the issue. **It is important that your client does not feel wounded, hurt, or further angered due to you demonstrating your power by ending the session.**

- **Be Concrete:** Many times a power struggle is over what could, would, or should happen. In these cases, the power struggle ends up going off course and you get caught up in hyperbole with little or no resolution. The key to deescalating it is to focus on concrete facts about the basis of the power struggle. But you must first remove yourself from the power struggle and reach an objective state. The other skills in this section can help you reach that point. Then, it is important to stay with the issue and make sure it is one issue. A single clearly defined problem is easier to contend with than three or four vague ones. Make sure you stay concrete and focused on one issue that is in the here and now. This could be what is going on in the session, how the client feels about you, or something else that has come up. Examine the single issue from an objective standpoint, break it down, and discuss viable options, noting that some issues have no resolution. Clients on the narcissistic spectrum have difficulty being concrete due to having a rich fantasy life and lessened ego resources. Teaching them the skills of being concrete and examining singular problems is valuable but notably difficult for this type of client.

Physical and Emotional Empathy

Having empathy is a valuable skill. It is not uncommon for individuals along the narcissistic spectrum to lack this particular skill. Empathy is the ability to recognize and interpret other people's emotions. Lack of empathy may manifest in two ways: 1) accurate interpretation of another individual's emotions with no concern for his or her distress and (2) inability to recognize and accurately interpret another individual's emotions. Both are possible in individuals along the narcissistic spectrum.

The first form of lack of empathy is a more pathological and volitional one, whereas the latter form is more indicative of alexithymia—difficulty identifying, describing, and working with one's own feelings, which is often associated with a lack of understanding of the feelings of others. When working with a client along this spectrum, it is important to discern between the two forms. The pathological form illustrates that the ability to empathize is present but not being utilized, and the second form illustrates a genuine inability to empathize altogether.

Individuals with both forms can benefit from physical and emotional empathy exercises. The client should be psychologically ready and have a desire to learn empathy skills. Learning empathy is like riding a bike: It is exceptionally difficult to teach someone to ride a bike that does not see the need and does not want to. When someone recognizes the need and benefit of riding a bike, he or she is intrinsically motivated for change and *will* learn. Your client needs to be intrinsically motivated to learn empathy and engage with others on a more intimate and genuine level.

Physical and Emotional Empathy

Directions: Practice these empathy-building exercises with someone you trust or your therapist. Some people find them odd or peculiar at first, but this is no different from when you first learned to ride a bike. It takes time to build a skill, and empathy is just that, a skill.

Physical:

- Find a person with whom you feel comfortable.

- Decide who will be the director and who will be the "mirror."

- Have the director begin a sequence of simple upper body movements that the "mirror" will imitate as if the director is looking directly into a mirror. For example, if the director raises his or her right arm, the "mirror" will raise his or her left arm.

- Reverse roles and repeat.

- Do this exercise a third time without appointing a specific director or mirror. Try to intuitively mirror the other person's movement as you switch back and forth between roles until each role becomes indistinguishable.

Emotional:

- Identify someone who is experiencing an emotion, such as sadness or elation. You can use YouTube to find examples of just about any emotion.

- Gather as much information as you can about his or her specific situation and what the root of the emotion(s) is.

- Find a secluded and safe location and try to mirror that person as accurately as you can from memory: Assume his or her body position, posture, tone, speech volume, gestures, and facial expressions.

After each exercise (physical and/or emotional) answer the following:

It felt (you can get the Emotions List from your therapist to help you)

_____

_____

_____ **to be** (write what you did during the physical and/or emotional exercise) _____

_____

_____

because (describe the root of your experience) _____

_____

Narcissism Key Target Areas for Treatment

Clients on the narcissistic spectrum typically lack awareness of the boundaries and perspectives of others, and this foundational deficit is rooted in several core factors, which are delineated by Benjamin:

- **Need for control**

- **Need to blame**

- **Tendency to attack**

- **Tendency to ignore the needs of others**

- **Intense love for self**

- **Tendency to neglect what is best for himself or herself**

- **Self-blame at imperfection or lack of adulation**

These core factors are sure to bring about one or several of the common narcissistic defenses listed below (Millon, et al. 2004; Thomas, 2010):

Repression	Unconscious mechanism to keep disturbing or threatening thoughts from becoming conscious.
Distortion	Reshaping external reality to suit inner needs, such as beliefs, hallucinations, and delusions. Sustains feelings of superiority, entitlement.
Recruitment	Enlisting the help of others who will support his or her distorted view.
Projection	Attributing own unacceptable thoughts, feelings, and motives to another person.
Denial	Blocking information from awareness to avoid seeing painful aspect of reality.

Next Steps

Managing defenses can be difficult and in some cases bring up countertransference reactions. (See the transference and countertransference exercises and Countertransference Scale in Part II, "Antisocial Personality Disorder Spectrum" for more information.) The best way to manage defense mechanisms and focus on core content is to be aware of which defense mechanism your client uses most often when confronted with the core issues listed previously. The following worksheet is designed to help you do that. After your client has completed the worksheet, ask yourself which defense mechanisms are being used most often and under what conditions?

Narcissism Key Target Areas for Treatment

Directions: Below is a list of common defense mechanisms or reactions in which one may engage when confronting important life issues. Circle which defense mechanism you would be most likely to use when you encounter each issue listed. This is a great opportunity to learn about yourself and how you see the world. This increases your personal power by increasing your self-awareness.

Repression	Unconscious mechanism to keep disturbing or threatening thoughts from becoming conscious.
Distortion	Reshapes external reality to suit inner needs, such as beliefs, hallucinations, and delusions. Sustains feelings of superiority, entitlement.
Recruitment	Enlisting the help of others who will support his or her distorted view.
Projection	Attributing own unacceptable thoughts, feelings, and motives to another person.
Denial	Blocking information from awareness to avoid seeing painful aspect of reality.

1. **Feel in control**
   Repression   Distortion   Recruitment   Projection   Denial

2. **Tendency to blame others**
   Repression   Distortion   Recruitment   Projection   Denial

3. **Tendency to attack others when disagreed with**
   Repression   Distortion   Recruitment   Projection   Denial

4. **Lessen others' needs**
   Repression   Distortion   Recruitment   Projection   Denial

5. **Love for self**
   Repression   Distortion   Recruitment   Projection   Denial

6. **Neglect what is best for me?**
   Repression   Distortion   Recruitment   Projection   Denial

7. **Self-blame when things are not perfect**
   Repression   Distortion   Recruitment   Projection   Denial

8. **Self-blame when I do not get attention I deserve**
   Repression   Distortion   Recruitment   Projection   Denial

Maladaptive Beliefs About Self and Emotions

Individuals along the narcissistic spectrum hold many maladaptive beliefs about themselves and their own emotions. A critical component of lessening narcissistic tendencies is for the client to work through these maladaptive beliefs about himself or herself and his or her emotions. It is expected that your client is going to intensely hold onto his or her judgment of others and situations, as well as the maladaptive beliefs that keep the narcissistic tendencies intact.

Next Steps

The worksheet that follows is designed to help you obtain critical information related to how your client on the narcissistic spectrum thinks and feels about himself or herself, how he or she manages negative feelings, and how he or she reacts when triggered by an adverse event, such as being told what to do at work. You will also be gaining information about whether he or she holds common negative opinions of himself or herself that are often found in these clients. The final three questions pertain to the client's willingness to learn to do things differently, improve emotional management, and improve self-concept.

It is important that your client on the narcissistic spectrum feels validated and supported by you so that he or she is comfortable enough to provide honest answers. Difficulty identifying and exploring these issues is common, and an atmosphere of trust is critical. A statement such as, "Many people find this to be a difficult task, but I believe you can do it" can provide needed reassurance and a sense of safety.

Beliefs About Self and Emotions

Directions: The statements below are designed to help you explore how you feel about yourself and your emotions. Answer each to the best of your ability. If you get stuck, which is not uncommon during this exercise, work with your therapist to get a better understanding of what response will fit for you.

I should always feel good about what I say and do because _____

_____

_____

_____

_____

I cannot stand it when _____

_____

_____

_____

_____

_____

If I do not feel happy or pleased with myself, I am a _____

because _____

_____

_____

_____

_____

_____

When I react by _____

I feel BETTER, WORSE, or the SAME (circle one).

I avoid the emotion _____ **most because** _____

_____

_____

_____

The statement "I am a loser and weak for feeling hurt" is TRUE or FALSE (circle one) **about me because** _____

_____

_____

_____

The statement "It is unacceptable to not feel happy all the time" is TRUE or FALSE (circle one) **about me because** _____

_____

_____

_____

I do believe I can learn a different way of doing things because _____

_____

_____

_____

One way to better manage my emotions is to _____

_____

_____

_____

One way to improve how I see myself is to _____

_____

_____

_____

Defuse Narcissistic Resistance

Resistance is inherent when working with an individual with a personality disorder, but this is of particular significance when working with the client on the narcissistic spectrum. Resistance is not always negative. It shows that your client has energy to protect himself or herself and has the motivation to promote his or her view of the world. Many therapists tend to misinterpret resistance as only a hindrance to the therapeutic progress, and they often attack it head on, causing a therapeutic disruption or slowdown.

Clinically attacking resistance in therapy is the personification of the old adage, "You can bring a horse to water, but you cannot make him drink." You can browbeat your client to the point that you are convinced that he or she will finally understand that drinking and drugging will ruin his or her life, he or she has no money because he or she keeps screaming and quitting his or her job, his or her spouse is leaving him or her because he or she continually demeans him or her, etc. This approach just does not work. Showing your client his or her maladaptive ways does not cause an epiphany that leads to behavioral and lifelong change. Changing maladaptive patterns to adaptive patterns has to come from working with core issues, and as you, the therapist, engage in core issues, resistance will surface.

Conceptualizing resistance as a natural process of therapy and a good sign changes the therapist's perspective and increases inroads to minimizing it. There are several therapeutic techniques that can be useful in lessening resistance in your clients on the narcissistic spectrum (Miller & Rollnick, 2002): reframing, simple reflection, double-sided reflection, clarification, focus shifting, and building autonomy.

Reframing	Creating an alternative way of looking at a situation, person, or relationship by changing its meaning.
Simple Reflection	Paraphrasing and/or restating both the feelings and words of the speaker to demonstrate awareness of the emotions to the client and expresses empathy.
Double-Sided Reflection	Reflecting both the current, resistant statement and a previous contradictory statement that the client has made.
Clarification	Validating verbal and non-verbal communication to determine its accuracy.
Focus Shifting	Moving attention away from the blockade and onto something more manageable.
Building Autonomy	Enhancing your client's right to participate and grow in treatment.

Using these techniques and mastering them will not only help to reduce resistance in your clients on the narcissistic spectrum, but in all of your clients. Like any new skill, it takes time and practice. The exercise that follows is meant to assist you in building your resistance defusing skills.

Following are examples of common statements made by clients on the narcissistic spectrum that indicate resistance, and in some cases cause the therapist to get off track or get lost in the pathology. Remember that the key to defusing resistance is working with it, not against it. I have provided you an example to illustrate each resistance defusing technique.

Example:

A couple has come for marital therapy, and the wife is resistant to attending.

Client: "Have you read that article by Beck in 1989?"

Therapist: "No, I have not [not looking shaken]."

Client: "You haven't?" [Looks at spouse annoyed.] "You have a degree, right?"

Therapist: "Yes."

Client: "You're licensed?"

Therapist: "Yes."

Client: "Wait a second." [Puts hands up in the air signaling stop.] "You have a degree, you have a license, and you have not read this article?" [Looks at spouse concerned.] "OK, *this* is who you want to see. Go ahead."

Possible responses:

Reframing: "You sound uncertain that I have the qualifications to help you."

Simple Reflection: "Like you, a lot of people are concerned that coming in for treatment will not help them to do things differently, but I have had a lot of success with couples striving to make a difference that works for them."

Double-Sided Reflection: "Sounds like you begrudgingly came in today and you're not sure I can help you do things differently. What do you think was effective about the Beck article that may help you both in this process?"

Clarification: "You look annoyed at hearing I have not read the Beck article, and you appear to be questioning your husband's choice to come to treatment."

Focus Shifting: "You were referred by Dr. Smith. Can you tell me what worked for you in your treatment with her?"

Building Autonomy: "One of the most important aspects of treatment is knowing that both parties have the right to choose to go forward and that it will be all of us working together to enhance your relationship and help you grow as individuals as well as within your marriage."

Defuse Narcissistic Resistance

Directions: Below is a series of resistance statements, each with two spaces to practice how you would respond using one or two of the techniques just presented. If you find yourself using one or two more often, try another to see if it fits. Learning resistance reduction techniques is no different from teaching your clients anxiety reduction techniques. The more you practice, the better you get, but if you only use these skills when you are in dire need, you increase the probability that you will falter.

"You're just not smart enough to work with someone like me."

1. _____

2. _____

"What do you think you could do for me to make me want to get better?"

1. _____

2. _____

"I know you want to help me, but what you're asking is just too hard."

1. _____

2. _____

"It's not that big of a deal [getting into a physical fight with his boss]. He needed to be taught a lesson, and now he has been."

1. _____

2. _____

"Working with you is so exhausting."

1. _____

2. _____

Avoiding Session Sabotage

The word sabotage is reported to have originated in the 15th century in what is now called Belgium, when workers threw their sabots (wooden shoes) into the wooden gears of the textile looms to break the cogs out of the fear that the automated machines that would render the human workers useless. This story is an interesting one, and it is applicable to the work we do with individuals who have personality disorders, specifically those on the narcissistic spectrum.

Despite having the best intentions, sometimes therapists unknowingly engage in behaviors that sabotage the therapy session. When working with clients on the narcissistic spectrum, many session-sabotaging behaviors derive from the clinician's reactions to client statements or behavior. The following exercise is designed to help therapists identify the six most common session-sabotaging behaviors and how to avoid them and encourage growth in your clients.

Directing/Advice Giving

Directing and advice giving typically occurs in session when the therapist is thrown off track, or in the case of the client on the narcissistic spectrum, when the client has triggered the therapist to prove competency or invoked a need to seem helpful, or, in a desperate act to promote change, the therapist begins to give advice on "how to live right." An additional factor that causes therapists to fall into sabotaging behavior is when they are under time constraints. This can include when the session time is running out or treatment is reaching an end.

How to do it differently:

- Take an internal reading as to how you are feeling about the client. Are you being triggered to prove yourself? If so, see the worksheets on transference and countertransference, the Countertransference Scale, or "Surmount the Power Struggle" in Part II on the antisocial personality spectrum.

- Advice is destructive in treatment and takes away the client's power and responsibility to choose; suggestions promote growth and success. Instead of giving advice, make a suggestion on what you think will help him or her.

- Map out your sessions, and come back to this timeline. Working with personality disorders takes years in most cases. The further along your client is on the narcissistic spectrum, the longer treatment is expected to take. Be willing to revise your timeline, if feasible, based on monetary issues, insurance, or other relevant factors.

Persuasion-Resistance Trap

The persuasion-resistance trap is typically derived from the therapist trying as hard as he or she can to get the client to change. Typically, the harder the therapist pulls, the more resistant the client is. Whereas narcissistic resistance comes from the client, persuasion-resistance may emanate from the therapist. The therapist wants to speed up the progress of treatment, so he or she tries to convince the client of what is in his or her best interest. The therapist wants to see gains in the client or to illustrate the value in the treatment process to the client, who is usually resistant to treatment in the first place.

How to do it differently:

- Stay with the client. Make sure you are not overly focused on visible results. Remember, many of the gains in treatment are not immediate and may not be noticeable to the client and/or therapist until days, weeks, months, or even years later.

- Remember, you will never be able to convince someone of anything he or she is not ready for. You cannot force him or her into a different way of living if he or she is not ready or willing!

Rescuing the Client

Therapists attempt to rescue the client for several reasons, and this sabotaging behavior is most likely to occur when working with the covert type of narcissism. (For more detail on this, see "Attachment and the Narcissistic Spectrum.") Covert narcissism is expressed in a very anxiety-driven, introverted, defensive, and vulnerable manner (a different form of narcissism than what most therapists expect), which can elicit an unexpected response in many therapists to protect and rescue the client; however, this is often the secondary gain that the client wants. The therapist may feel excessive enthusiasm to rescue the client, and he or she may even believe he or she knows "just the thing" to resolve the stressor. Rescuing the client manifests as urging and pleading with the client to stop engaging in particular maladaptive behaviors. The therapist may say, "I want the best for you, please stop getting high! Can't you see what you're doing to yourself?" I have also seen this sabotaging behavior in the form of role breaking, which can include doing home visits or offering money to clients.

How to do it differently:

- Stay in your lane. You are the therapist, not the hero. You should never swoop into your client's life and attempt to rescue him or her from his or her maladaptive beliefs and behaviors.

- Consult with a colleague or supervisor you trust and describe the tendency you are seeing. If you see it, you can change it!

- Rescuing has short-term results with long-term consequences. Allow your client to experience dissonance. He or she has to be uncomfortable to move outside of his or her comfort zone. Removing this discomfort prematurely will result in further manifestation of pathology.

Getting Lost With the Client

I have had some clients with amazing life stories. I will admit that I am a sucker for a fascinating story. However, I also know that I need to be aware of this about myself, and whereas the many facets of someone's life experience can provide me the information I need to help him or her, this does not include the voyeuristic component of the story itself. Very early in my career, I noticed that my desire to help often got intertwined with the interesting components of my clients' stories, and we would get lost in them, using up valuable session time.

How to do it differently:

- Reassess goal direction and content. Focus on operationally defining goals and course of treatment.

- Be upfront about being lost in the story and address the components or theme of the story and how it relates to the client's maladaptive beliefs and behaviors and core content.

Client Overload

Therapists tend to overload their clients with information when they want to show how skilled they are, which creates a "shotgun effect," presenting a broad and unfocused picture of ways to change. This can happen when there are only a few minutes left in the session and the therapist feels compelled to give advice or suggestions in the time that is left. This causes the client to fall into a passive role, feel overwhelmed, and retain little to none of the information.

How to do it differently:

- Keep session momentum slow so the client can grasp the information being provided. It is OK to not get to everything.

- Be sure to impart information at appropriate times along the way. This prevents the therapist from saving up all "the gems" in treatment until the end.

- If you have a lot of suggestions and recommendations, make a list between sessions to give to the client. You can even use session time to process which ones seem the most viable for him or her to attempt.

Pursue Problems and Weaknesses

Therapists can become so focused on problems and weaknesses or diagnoses that they forget to assess the client's strengths and positive features. This tends to cause clients, especially those on the narcissistic spectrum, to feel frustrated and annoyed and this further encourages resistance and acting out behaviors. It is just as important to note what your client can do well as it is to point out issues and concerns that are present in his or her life. A dogmatic approach to problems and weaknesses will sabotage therapeutic success every time.

How to do it differently:

- Remember, you are not the moral compass for your clients, and policing their behavior only causes them to distance themselves from you.

- Assess your role in your client's life and within the process of therapy. Do you fall into a governor/overseer role? If so, you may want to examine this with a colleague or during supervision.

- Try to use your client's problems and weaknesses as opportunities to succeed and overcome challenges with your assistance by building strengths and prosocial behaviors. Every client has strengths; find them, use them, and enhance them. This workbook is designed to help you achieve this treatment goal.

Part Four
Histrionic Personality Disorder Spectrum

Histrionic Personality and Its Subtypes

Histrionic personality consists of intense emotionality and attention-seeking behaviors. Histrionic behavior, like narcissism, is prevalent in our society. According to the DSM-5, the prevalence of Histrionic Personality Disorder (HPD) was found to be 1.84% in the early 2000s, and although HPD is diagnosed more often in female clients, "the sex ratio is not significantly different from the sex ratio of females within the respective clinical setting. In contrast, some APA studies using structured assessments report similar prevalence rates among males and females." Thus, HPD can manifest in both male and female clients.

The components that make up the histrionic spectrum include the following:

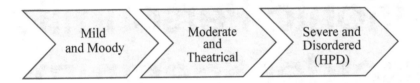

The individual that fits into the **mild and moody** category tends to be friendly and generally social, emotionally expressive, and socially gregarious, with a twinge of suspiciousness, superficiality, and lacking in substance. These individuals are likely to have friends, potentially long-term, but are highly reactive. Their reactions are not intensely disruptive but often get attention due to how disproportionate they are in comparison to the originating stimulus.

When an individual in this category reports issues and occurrences in his or her life to friends, family, or a therapist, he or she tends to sound fake or like he or she is lying due to the lack of information or substance included. The person's emotional overreaction combined with the lack of details causes others to feel they are being lied to. When an individual's environment does not alter this behavior, and in some cases rewards him or her for it, the individual moves further along the continuum to more moderate and theatrical beliefs and behaviors.

At this point along the continuum, the **moderate and theatrical** individual begins to persistently seek the attention of others as a source of validation of self. Due to their intensive external view and lack of sense of self, the person develops a level of shallowness and flightiness that can be grating to others. He or she tends to be seen as annoying, which causes the withdrawal of others or in some cases, complete social rejection.

When this individual encounters rejection, the response is disproportionately intense, and he or she seeks to fill that void with some form of attention. He or she must obtain recognition of the self by an external object to repair his or her sense of self-worth. In treatment, such an individual is likely to test the therapist's patience and resolve through demanding constant validation. If the therapist does not meet this need, the moderate and theatrical client will terminate treatment and seek another therapist who will. "Therapist hopping" is not uncommon for these individuals. As with the earlier phase of the HPD continuum, if the individual does not experience dissonance severe enough to cause change, he or she may move to the level of severe and disordered or HPD.

Histrionic personality disorder (HPD) is an extreme form of theatrical behavior that disrupts the individual's socioeconomic functioning; this entails disruptions in occupational and personal realms. HPD is often seen and referred to as "BPD light." This is due to its many similarities in presentation, but the individual with true HPD lacks the destructiveness, angry disruptions in close relationships, and chronic feelings of deep emptiness and identity disturbance often seen in clients with BPD. As in all personality disorders, the pathology of HPD forms a positive feedback loop, which reinforces itself so that the world of the individual with HPD justifies his or her maladaptive beliefs and behaviors. These include the following:

- **Has to be the center of attention**
- **Is quick to intimacy**
- **Displays exaggerated emotion**
- **Seeks attention via appearance**
- **Displays shallow emotions**
- **Engages in provocative behaviors**
- **Is suggestible**
- **Makes statements that lack detail**

Histrionic personality disorder is not an impossible disorder to treat. The worksheets and exercises in this section address critical therapist and client factors to attenuate histrionic spectrum beliefs and behaviors and encourage greater therapeutic success.

Histrionic Personality Spectrum

The histrionic personality spectrum consists of Mild and Moody, Moderate and Theatrical, and HPD. It is critical to identify where your client is emotionally, how he or she sees his or her world, and what his or her subsequent reactions to it are, which can seriously impact socioeconomic functioning and therapeutic success. The Emotional Spectrum Worksheet, which follows, is designed to help the client by encouraging insight into his or her emotional and interpersonal reactions. The three components along this spectrum have several factors in common that can assist you, the therapist, in determining strengths and weaknesses, as well as emotional outlook of your client. Each factor is listed on the Emotional Spectrum Assessment. These factors include the following:

- **Impulsivity**
- **Need for attention**
- **Suggestibility**
- **Sociability**
- **Pleasure orientation**
- **Self-knowledge**
- **Reality**
- **Self-restraint**
- **Mood stability**
- **Friendships**

Next Steps

Assessing each of these factors is critical to gauging therapeutic success with individuals on the histrionic spectrum. It is inherent when working with these individuals to realize that their emotions and interpersonal interactions will ebb and flow. Giving this worksheet at key times or on a continual basis can help identify how your client responds to his or her environmental expectations, stressors, and successes.

Results of this worksheet will be more extreme the further your client is along the histrionic spectrum. As therapy progresses and your client learns to attenuate histrionic spectrum impulses and responses, results will correlate by decreasing in severity.

Emotional Spectrum

Directions: Complete the Emotional Spectrum Worksheet to help you become more aware of your current emotions and keep track of changes across sessions. Be as honest as you can, and do not censor your responses. Each response represents how you feel right now.

Impulsivity

None   0 1 2 3 4 5   Highly Impulsive

Need for Attention

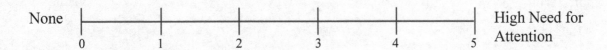

None   0 1 2 3 4 5   High Need for Attention

Suggestibility

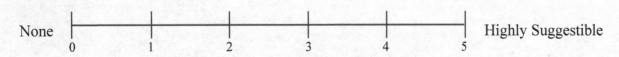

None   0 1 2 3 4 5   Highly Suggestible

Sociability

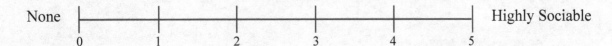

None   0 1 2 3 4 5   Highly Sociable

Pleasure Orientation

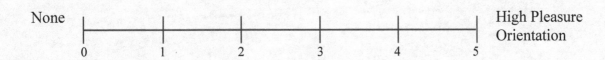

None   0 1 2 3 4 5   High Pleasure Orientation

Self-Knowledge (How Well You Know Self)

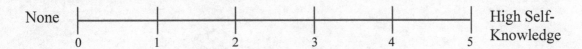

None   0 1 2 3 4 5   High Self-Knowledge

Reality (Grounded in What Is Real in Life)

Reality   0 1 2 3 4 5   Fantasy

Self-Restraint

None 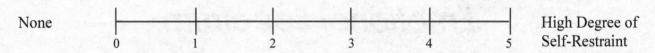 High Degree of
Self-Restraint

Mood Stability

Unlikely
to Fluctuate 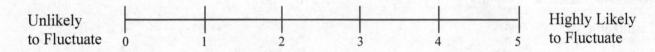 Highly Likely
to Fluctuate

Friendships

Very
Short-Term  Last a Long
Time

Histrionic/Borderline Distinction

Histrionic personality disorder (HPD) and borderline personality disorder (BPD) have much in common on the surface. HPD has been called "BPD light" due to having very similar presentations, but HPD lacks the intensity of emptiness, self-destructiveness, angry disruptions in close relationships, and identity disturbance that are evident in individuals with BPD. Knowing these distinctions does not necessarily make it any easier to discern between the two when first encountering an individual with one of these disorders. Following is an outline of key distinguishing characteristics to help you identify which diagnosis is appropriate.

Histrionic Personality Disorder	Borderline Personality Disorder
• Need for approval • Attention-seeking and seductive behavior • High need for attention and will do anything to acquire it • Constantly seeking reassurance or approval • Excessive dramatics with exaggerated displays of emotion • Excessive sensitivity to criticism or disapproval • Inappropriately seductive appearance or behavior • Overly concerned with physical appearance • Tendency to believe that relationships are more intimate than they actually are • Self-centeredness, uncomfortable when not the center of attention • Low tolerance for frustration or delayed gratification • Rapidly shifting emotional states that appear shallow to others • Opinions are easily influenced by other people, but difficult to back up with details • May originate in childhood trauma, death in the family, and lack of love as a child	• Exhibits intense and unstable moods, behavior and relationships • History of reckless behavior and suicidal tendencies • Extreme reactions • Intense relationships • Impulsive decisions and behavior • Suicidal tendencies • Extensive mood swings • Feelings of emptiness • Intensive and uncontrollable anger • May originate from a history of childhood trauma, brain abnormalities, genetic predisposition, and family environment

Next Steps

After going through the list of identifiers side by side, several key differences between HPD and BPD emerge. First, the individual with BPD displays more intensity in his or her presentation and approach to life. The HPD individual's goal is to be seen and appreciated, but his or her needs are met in a less destructive and violent manner, which is nonetheless detrimental to his or her socioeconomic functioning. When you, the therapist, encounter an individual that seems to be blurring the line between these two disorders, there are some key questions to ask that will help you distinguish between HPD and BPD. The following worksheet addresses the key points in making this distinction.

The responses illustrate the factors listed in the chart on the previous page. The individual with BPD is likely to be impulsive, reckless, and revenge driven, toward both himself or herself and the object of other (e.g., significant other, family member). The individual with HPD is likely to have less intense and harmful responses. In many cases, he or she will have trouble answering the question "My emptiness feels like" because he or she does not feel empty. When answering the final question pertaining to suicidal behaviors, the individual with BPD is likely to pick any of the responses, but the individual with HPD is unlikely to pick "Relieve my pain," "Show a loved one how much I hurt," "Get revenge," or "Make sure people know I am alive." These responses help clarify which diagnosis is present. If your client meets criteria for both disorders, you will find that all of the questions in this worksheet will be completed, and answers will have the following themes: "I need to be in the spotlight" and "Help me—I am drowning and stuck." These are core structural components of both disorders.

Actions/Reactions

Directions: In the space that follows, write how you would react or would feel in each situation.

When a relationship ends, how do you feel and tend to react?

_____

_____

_____

_____

When I feel I am being ignored, I will _____

_____

_____

_____

My emptiness feels like _____

_____

_____

_____

_____

When I meet someone, I know we are soulmates because _____

_____

_____

_____

_____

I will often think about hurting myself to: (circle all that apply)

Relieve my pain   Get attention   Show a loved one how much I hurt

Get revenge   See who cares   Make sure people know I am alive

Attachment and the Histrionic Spectrum

Individuals along the histrionic spectrum attach to others quickly and easily, especially within the therapeutic relationship. Treating attachment issues is a complex process and involves identifying and working with the insecure attachment pattern and recreating a more secure attachment in its place. The therapeutic environment and relationship is ideal for doing this. To examine attachment and the histrionic spectrum, we use the model devised by Bartholomew and Horowitz shown here:

	Positive View of Self	**Negative View of Self**
Positive View of Others	**Secure Attachment** Hopeful Satisfied Trusting Self-Disclosing	**Preoccupied Attachment** Hopeless Dissatisfied Trusting Self-Disclosing
Negative View of Others	**Dismissing Attachment** Hopeful Satisfied Distrusting Non-Disclosing	**Fearful Attachment** Hopeless Dissatisfied Distrusting Non-Disclosing

The individual along the histrionic spectrum falls within the preoccupied attachment style. Individuals in this attachment category tend to view others in a positive light and themselves in a negative light. The individual on the histrionic spectrum tends to fall into distress, exhibit poor emotional control, and express symptomatology aimed at the self, as well as the concrete view that others will "save" him or her. Due to the view that others are good and the self is bad, the individual on the histrionic spectrum tends to be vulnerable, relationship seeking, and highly sensitive to rejection. These behaviors and feelings manifest quickly in the therapeutic relationship.

Next Steps

The worksheet that follows is designed to elicit responses related to attachment and how the client perceives and manages attachment disruptions. The further along the spectrum he or she is, the greater difficulty he or she will exhibit in responding, because the worksheet relates directly to the core content of the preoccupied attachment style, which includes quickly connecting to others through self-disclosure and trust.

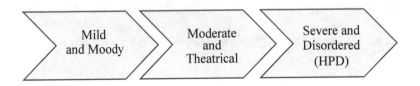

Mild and Moody → Moderate and Theatrical → Severe and Disordered (HPD)

The worksheet also addresses the value of self that is often seen as dissatisfying and hopeless, as the HPD individual does not feel that he or she can provide emotional security and confidence to engage in genuine relationships and develop reciprocal connections with others.

The client on the histrionic spectrum is likely to embellish his or her responses in an effort to entertain you or keep you interested in working with him or her. In a very open and non-threatening manner, ask your client to fill out the worksheet and discuss his or her answers. He or she will be highly sensitive to feedback, if the client has answered honestly. Remember, every answer is a valuable one. If your client gives an answer that you know is false, that still provides useful data in treatment. All information, even a lie, is fodder for treatment. Your client's answers can be seen as a projective.

Viewpoint

Directions: Write your immediate thought after each sentence stem. *Do not edit your thoughts.*

I know others are nurturing and loving because they _____

_____

_____

_____

_____

_____

If someone really loves me, he or she will show recognition and admiration by _____

_____

_____

_____

_____

_____

I like to be the center of attention because _____

_____

_____

_____

_____

_____

_____

The best way to be entertaining and seductive is by _____

_____

_____

_____

I feel most attractive when _____

_____

_____

_____

_____

People are the most trusting when they _____

_____

_____

_____

_____

_____

I feel connected to someone when _____

_____

_____

_____

_____

_____

When I am alone, I feel _____

_____

_____

_____

_____

Histrionic Spectrum and Suicide Risk

In the Diagnostic and Statistical Manual, Third Edition, there was a criterion for HPD that specifically addressed suicidality in these individuals: it stated that people on the histrionic spectrum are "prone to manipulative, suicidal threats, gestures, or attempts." This statement was removed from subsequent DSM volumes as many argued that this criterion is not highly characteristic of the disorder. Though this criterion was removed after the DSM-III, it is still likely that individuals further along the histrionic spectrum may engage in suicidal behaviors.

Suicidal gestures by individuals along the histrionic spectrum are typically made in an attempt to influence others to modify their behaviors. In many cases, suicidal gestures are acts of absolute trust in the other person who is the identified object/savior. Benjamin described a perfect illustration of an HPD individual "… locking the bathroom door during a marital fight, overdosing, and then being angry because the spouse took so long to break open the door."

Be prepared to address suicidal issues when working with individuals along the histrionic spectrum. Several key factors need to be considered, which include statements of self-harm; psychological, emotional, behavioral, and situational factors; whether the client has a suicide plan; what the person believes will happen to the living after he or she is dead; and prevention. The final and critical factor to consider is the client's openness and willingness to tell you (the therapist) about any suicidal ideation or intent he or she is experiencing.

Next Steps

The following is a worksheet to address Suicidal Risk. At the bottom of the form is a signature and date line for the client to complete for the therapist's records. This can be helpful in securing an agreement to discuss these issues in session, as well as ascertaining the presence or absence of suicidal ideation or intent.

As in any case where you are dealing with the possible loss of life, consultation and potential referral to a hospital or emergency room may be necessary. Know the guidelines in your state to be sure you are following the appropriate steps to manage the situation.

Suicide Risk

Place a check (✓) next to the following statement(s) that most accurately identify how you are feeling. (Mark all that apply.)

_____ I am going to kill myself.

_____ You are going to be sorry when I am gone.

_____ My life is not worth living anymore.

_____ I have thoughts of ending my life, but I would not carry them out.

_____ I do not have any thoughts of killing myself.

Place a check (✓) next to any of the following emotions that you have experienced in the past 2 weeks. (Mark all that apply.)

_____ Long-term depression   _____ Feeling overwhelmed

_____ Feeling helpless   _____ Feeling sad

_____ Feeling hopeless   _____ Feeling unimportant

Place a check (✓) next to any of the following that you have experienced in the past 2 weeks. (Mark all that apply.)

_____ Preoccupation with death   _____ Poor concentration

_____ Lack of appetite/overeating   _____ Isolation

_____ Sleep disturbances   _____ Crying

Place a check (✓) next to any of the following behaviors have you engaged in during the past 2 weeks. (Mark all that apply.)

_____ Low self-esteem   _____ Giving away important things

_____ Inability to perform daily tasks   _____ Lack of interest in things previously enjoyed

_____ Previous suicide attempts   _____ Sudden refraining from activities with family and friends

_____ Writing a suicide note

_____ Engaging in risky or impulsive behavior   _____ Sudden unexplained recovery from depression, sudden positive outlook

_____ Sudden poor school or job performance

Place a check (✓) next to any of the following situations you have been in during the past 2 weeks. (Mark all that apply.)

___ School or career problems   ___ Relationship break-up /separation/divorce

___ Loss of job/career   ___ Multiple losses

___ Death of a loved one or peer   ___ Terminal illness

___ Suicide of a loved one or peer

If you were to harm yourself, how would you do it?

_____

_____

_____

_____

What would you hope would happen after you killed yourself?

_____

_____

_____

_____

What would prevent you from harming yourself? (e.g., religion, family, friends, children, pets)

_____

_____

_____

_____

If you were thinking about harming yourself, would you tell me?

☐ Yes   ☐ No

_____   _____
Client Signature   Date

Flirtation, Avoidance, and Inauthenticity

Three common concerns related to the treatment of individuals on the histrionic spectrum are flirtation, avoidance, and inauthenticity. It is important to note that these behaviors are not conscious but have developed over time as maladaptive responses that have worked in getting these clients' needs met. In session, these individuals know just when to engage in such behaviors. They are instinctive responses to environmental and psychological stimuli, and many therapists unwittingly get on the roller coaster with these clients. These maladaptive responses can significantly derail therapeutic progress and later success.

Next Steps

The Event, Need, Response Worksheet is designed to create awareness of behaviors in which your client engages to get his or her needs met. Each of the events listed was chosen to address the tendency of people on the histrionic spectrum to engage in flirtation, avoidance, or inauthenticity. Each of these three goals/needs may not be conscious to your client, and his or her goal/need may not be called flirtation, avoidance, or inauthenticity.

When you review your client's responses, be sure to look for themes and assess the likelihood of a positive and reinforcing pattern of maladaptive responses. Individuals along the histrionic spectrum are well known for self-sabotaging and overreacting in various situations while at the same time possessing little insight into their behaviors and the probable outcomes. This worksheet is designed to help your client build that skill and awareness.

Event, Need, Response

Directions: For each event, list what goal or need it brings up for you and then indicate how you would go about getting that goal/need met. A sample has been provided for you. Some people use many different behaviors to get their goal/need met, and some use a few "tried and true" methods. Answer each as honestly and completely as you can. Do you see a theme in your responses?

Event	Goal/Need	Response to get needs met
Party where you know few people	*Be noticed*	*Wear tight dress; meet every guy/girl in the place*
A friend is upset about losing a relationship		
Feeling lonely at home alone		
Someone attractive flirts with you		
Someone does not find you attractive		
Your friend got a new partner, who makes a pass at you		
You do not feel needed by friends		
You do not feel needed by family		
Car breaks down on the freeway		
You feel connected to someone you just met		

Histrionic Client Dangers

Many therapists do not feel that the client on the histrionic spectrum is a dangerous one, especially compared with antisocial and borderline clients. However, this is a misconception that can cause an unwitting therapist to lose his or her license or much more. The client on the histrionic spectrum has honed his or her ability to sense need and respond to it in a pathological manner. For example, he or she may present as needy when the therapist feels ineffective or lonely in his or her own life. The therapist then feels a greater connection to the client, as he or she has provided a sense of fulfillment and usefulness; this gives the client on the histrionic spectrum a "special client" status. Due to this, the therapist extends sessions, schedules the client at the end of the day, self-discloses more often, and finds himself or herself thinking about the client between sessions. These are all early indicators of an increase in the probability of inappropriate behavior on the part of the therapist, and the client is likely to respond to the added attention and special treatment, as this meets his or her core structure need.

Next Steps

The Safe Dozen Worksheet, which follows, is composed of 12 critical questions every therapist should ask himself or herself when working with any client with a Cluster B diagnosis, especially the client on the histrionic spectrum.

The Boundary Securement Guidelines help to protect the therapist. The best way to maintain appropriate boundaries is by maintaining good, clear communication. Risky situations that increase boundary violations should be avoided, and proper boundaries should be communicated clearly and early in the treatment process. The boundary securement guidelines are presented to help prevent boundary violations and avoid complaints of sexual misconduct.

The Safe Dozen

Directions: Answer each question honestly as to how you perceive your relationship with this client. This exercise is to help you take notice of any favoritism or feelings that may be developing between you and your client. If you find yourself moving toward behaviors or having thoughts that others may find inappropriate between a therapist and client, you should seek consultation or enter therapy yourself and consider referring this client to another therapist.

1. Is this in my client's best interest?	Yes	No
2. Are my client's needs being met?	Yes	No
3. Will this impact the quality of service I am providing?	Yes	No
4. Am I willing to consult a colleague?	Yes	No
5. Will my case notes be honest and clear about each session?	Yes	No
6. Would this be viewed negatively by my client's family or significant other?	Yes	No
7. Do I treat this client differently (e.g., extended sessions, amount of self-disclosure)?	Yes	No
8. Is this client "special" to me?	Yes	No
9. Would an outsider see me as taking advantage of this client?	Yes	No
10. Does this benefit me more than the client?	Yes	No
11. Does my behavior go against ethical guidelines or provisions?	Yes	No
12. Do I find myself thinking about or fantasizing about the client?	Yes	No

Boundary Securement

The following 12 guidelines are to ensure solid boundaries and will help protect therapists from engaging in inappropriate behaviors with a client on the histrionic spectrum or any other client. If your responses on The Safe Dozen Worksheet bring up concerns, do not ignore them; embrace them and make sure you are following these 12 guidelines:

1. Be aware of your client's past, such as a tendency to engage in romantic relationships with authority figures.

2. Refrain from using gestures, expressions, tone of voice, or any other behavior that your client may interpret as seductive, sexually provocative, or sexually abusive.

3. Do not make sexual references to a client's body or clothing.

4. Do not make sexual references or comments to a client.

5. Do not engage in any contact that can be seen as sexual, from touching to intercourse.

6. Do not ask details of sexual history or sexual likes/dislikes unless directly related to the purpose of the consultation.

7. Do not meet the client outside of session for any reason.

8. Do not talk about your own sexual preferences, fantasies, problems, activities, or performance.

9. Learn to detect and deflect seductive clients and control the therapeutic setting.

10. Be sure to consult a colleague about seductive clients; this helps to ensure that both client and therapist are engaging in appropriate interactions.

11. Be aware of proximity between you and your client.

12. Maintain good records that reflect any questions of a sexual nature and document any and all comments or concerns made by a client related to alleged sexual abuse, and any other unusual incident that may occur during the course of or after an appointment.

Emotional and Behavioral Record

For the histrionic individual, seeing how his or her emotions influence his or her behavior is very difficult. Insight is a key component in linking emotional and behavioral expression. Emotional and behavioral insight entails one's ability to self-monitor and self-examine; these two key components are impaired in individuals along the histrionic spectrum. Many maladaptive behaviors along the spectrum are derived from primary emotions, which serve to keep the client in control of his or her interpersonal and professional life.

Gaining insight into how these primary emotions influence your client's behavior provides him or her with the necessary tools to then control the behaviors and compulsions that have historically caused him or her to lose employment, friends, and significant others.

Next Steps

The Emotional and Behavioral Record Worksheet will assist you in helping your client recognize how his or her emotions influence his or her behavior and the probable outcome of that behavior. It may be beneficial to fill out the first one or two entries in session to ensure the client understands how to appropriately complete the exercise.

Emotional and Behavioral Record

Directions: Identify the first (or primary) emotion you feel following a particular behavior. The primary or motivating emotion may be fleeting and hard to recognize. It is what should be addressed in treatment to best gain understanding and control over emotions that drive maladaptive or negative behaviors. The secondary, or surface, emotion is the expressed emotion that may come after the primary emotion and may be easier to recognize. Secondary emotions may be hiding the more central primary emotions. Finally, list what outcome is expected from behaving in that manner. See examples below to assist you in filling out the worksheet.

Behavior	Primary Emotion	Secondary Emotion	Probable Outcome
Hit coworker	*Fear*	*Anger*	*Lose my employment*
Slept with friend's boyfriend	*Abandonment*	*Sadness*	*Lose my friend*
Purposely wore see-through blouse with no bra	*Out of control*	*Sexy*	*Unlikely to get the promotion and continue to get ignored at work*
Screamed at cashier	*Ignored*	*Rage*	*Asked to leave the store with my groceries*

False Self/True Self

We all have a false self and a true self. The false self is the protective aspect of our core personality that is designed to shield the true self from hurt and vulnerability. Clients on the histrionic spectrum learn to mask their true self with false presentations. These false self-presentations manifest as surface structure behaviors and are responses to unwanted and dissonant stimuli from friends, loved ones, employers, or anyone else within their world. This pattern of behavior is typically learned very early. Over time, the false self gains dominance and stunts growth.

The true self is the aspect of the individual's core personality that experiences a genuine conceptualization of the world and his or her emotions without distortion. The true self wants to learn about life and grow, whereas the false self is trying to survive and protect the true self from pain. When working with a client and trying to assess and strengthen the true self, therapists must slow him or her down and have him or her learn to distinguish between the false self and true self reactions.

Next Steps

False Self/True Self Worksheet is an excellent exercise to use at various times throughout treatment as your client begins to lessen his or her false self and live his or her life more honestly through the true self.

False Self/True Self

Many people have two aspects of who they are, a false self and a true self. The false self is what is built up over the years to manage pain, sadness, disappointment, and other negative emotions. This false self often drives behaviors that produce negative outcomes, such as loss of love, employment, and relationships. An individual's true self is an expression of what is genuinely inside himself or herself that is not influenced by the adverse factors of the false self. The true self is often honest and balanced in decision-making and is also representative of who one really is.

Directions: Identify a situation and write how you responded using your false self or true self. The object is to bring into awareness the various aspects of your true self. Expression of one's true self often lessens depression, anxiety, regret, and other negative emotions. An example is provided.

Situation	False Self	True Self
Disrespected by someone I considered to be a friend	*Punched her, kicked her, and spit on her*	*Told her how her behavior made me feel and how I deserve to be respected*

Self-Worth Enhancement

Self-worth is impacted by what we think about our successes and failures, the experiences we have in life, and the influence we have on them. Self-worth is affected by many factors, such as thoughts and perceptions about the self, how others react to us, illness, culture, and past experiences at home, school/work, and other settings. Individuals along the histrionic spectrum are likely to have a very fragile and low sense of self-worth.

Early relationships with caregivers and other important individuals often lay the foundation for later pathology, and they are also critical in designing the frame for self-worth. Many beliefs clients hold about themselves reflect messages they have received from these people over time. Many individuals on the histrionic spectrum received mostly negative feedback from these early relationships and were often criticized, teased, or devalued, and are highly likely to struggle with low self-worth as a result. Psychopathology and self-worth are not mutually exclusive. If you enhance your client's sense of self-worth, you can lessen the adverse impact of maladaptive patterns and related psychopathology.

Next Steps

The Self-Worth Enhancement Worksheet will aid in identifying troubling situations, negative emotions, positive and negative thoughts within these situations, factors related to managing these situations, self-worth enhancing emotions, and alternative behaviors your client may identify to build his or her sense of self-worth. This is an excellent worksheet to use in multiple times in session to gauge the progress and growth of self-worth.

Self-Worth Enhancement

Directions: List three situations that you feel lessen your self-worth or make you feel bad about yourself. This can include situations when you feel judged, forgotten, not the center of attention, etc.

Situation 1: _____

_____

_____

Situation 2: _____

_____

_____

Situation 3: _____

_____

_____

Circle which emotion(s) fit the corresponding situation that lessens your self-worth. (Circle all that apply.)

Situation 1.	Anxious	Grieving	Unsupported	Humiliated	Other:
	Worthless	Confused	Conflicted	Overwhelmed	_____
Situation 2.	Anxious	Grieving	Unsupported	Humiliated	Other:
	Worthless	Confused	Conflicted	Overwhelmed	_____
Situation 3.	Anxious	Grieving	Unsupported	Humiliated	Other:
	Worthless	Confused	Conflicted	Overwhelmed	_____

List your positive and negative thoughts and self-talk while you are in each of these situations:

Situation 1: _____

_____

_____

Situation 2: _____

_____

_____

Situation 3: _____

_____

_____

List the outcomes of how these thoughts help or hinder you in managing these situations:

Situation 1: _____

_____

_____

Situation 2: _____

_____

_____

Situation 3: _____

_____

_____

Circle which emotion(s) fit the corresponding situation that would help enhance your self-worth. (Circle all that apply.)

Situation 1.	Compassionate	Calm	Worthy	Valued	Other:
	Kind	Optimistic	Forgiven	Self-Respectful	_____
Situation 2.	Compassionate	Calm	Worthy	Valued	Other:
	Kind	Optimistic	Forgiven	Self-Respectful	_____
Situation 3.	Compassionate	Calm	Worthy	Valued	Other:
	Kind	Optimistic	Forgiven	Self-Respectful	_____

List what you could/would do differently in these situations to enhance and encourage the emotions that build your self-worth:

Situation 1: _____

_____

_____

Situation 2: _____

_____

_____

Situation 3: _____

_____

_____

Managing the Session With a Histrionic Spectrum Client

Therapists must be cognizant of the unique issues that arise when working with clients along the histrionic spectrum in order to maintain control of sessions. Failure to maintain session control with these clients, as with any client who has a personality disorder, can cause significant problems for the client and therapist alike.

Next Steps

Managing the session with a client on the histrionic spectrum requires awareness of the problem components, what defenses are being employed, what is motivating the client, and what is the benefit to the client of using these maladaptive defenses to disrupt therapeutic progression. However, understanding these aspects alone is not enough to garner control of the session. It is also important to bring to awareness related past experiences and how they manifest and are perceived, as well as what techniques would lessen their expression.

Identification of disruptive session behaviors can assist the therapist in moving treatment forward and overcoming or avoiding problematic behaviors. As stated previously, one of these key aspects is assessing the client's motivation for and benefit (direct and indirect) from disrupting the session. Additionally, assessing the client's underlying core beliefs and surface-oriented automatic thoughts is critical, as is finding a suitable method to lessen these issues. This process not only brings to the forefront core client issues, but also decreases the likelihood of defenses and therapeutic sabotage.

The following worksheet is meant for therapists and is an excellent additive to supervision when working with a client on the histrionic spectrum or any complex client. If you find it difficult to answer some of the questions posed in the worksheet, the exercise will help you increase awareness of important aspects on which to focus during your next treatment session. Know your client and his or her core structure, and you will reach therapeutic progression and ultimately, success.

It may also be beneficial to go over the results with a colleague to further enhance your understanding of these and other complex client types and techniques for session management.

Managing the Session With a Histrionic Spectrum Client

Directions: Place a check (✓) next to the histrionic spectrum component that is causing difficulty in the therapeutic session. Factors that can cause difficulty in the session include anything that stalls forward movement, blocks insight, encourages a power struggle, or brings about intense defenses in therapist and client, among other things.

Histrionic Spectrum Components
Fear of rejection
Attempts to seek approval and avoid rejection
Minimal attempts at problem-solving
Over-reaction to rejection
Intensive attention-seeking behavior
Belief that he or she cannot manage his or her own life
Poor emotional management
Focus on responses of others
Little focus on own thoughts and feelings
Unclear identity
Continual crises in relationships

Which defense is your client employing to disrupt session progression? Check (✓) all that apply.

	Denial		Passive-aggressive behavior
	Distortion (reshapes reality to meet inner needs)		Dissociation (modifies personal identity to avoid distress)
	Splitting (has "all good or all bad" mentality)		Externalization (perceives own moods, conflicts, attitudes in others)
	Blocking (inhibits clear thinking temporarily)		Repression (expels or withholds ideas from consciousness)
	Introjection (internalizes the other person and his or her values)		Intellectualization (attends to external reality to avoid feelings)
	Somatization (converts mental pain into physical pain)		Sexualization (attributes sexual significance to object or function)
	Projection (attributes own feelings to others)		Humor (uses humor to protect self and other from negative emotions)
	Displacement (shifts emotion from one concept/object to another)		Suppression (acknowledges discomfort but minimizes it)

How are the components and the defenses disrupting therapeutic progression?

_____

_____

What are the motivations behind and the benefit of disrupting therapeutic progression?

_____

_____

What is the early experience or childhood precursor related to the development of the components and defenses?

_____

_____

What are the core beliefs related to the components and defenses?

_____

_____

What are the automatic thoughts related to the components and defenses?

_____

_____

What can you use that can reduce or replace the dysfunctional component and defense? Check (✓) all of the potential treatment techniques that fit with your client's view and approach to the world. Many of the techniques to help manage session disruptions are described on worksheets in this workbook (in this section or others); remember that antisocial, narcissistic, borderline, and histrionic spectrum disorders have many similarities, so these treatments can be used effectively for more than one disorder.

	Reality testing		Mindfulness techniques (see worksheets in DBT Mindfulness section)
	Relaxation techniques		Physical and Emotional Empathy Worksheet
	Anxiety reduction		Wants To/Shoulds Balance Worksheet
	Exposure		D-E-A-R M-A-N Worksheet
	Problem-solving		Acting Opposite Emotion Worksheet
	Self-Worth Enhancement Worksheet		Unhealthy to Healthy Coping Worksheet
	Enhancement of true self (see False Self/ True Self Worksheet)		Four Keys to Crisis Survival Worksheet
	Sleep hygiene		Willingness Over Willfulness Worksheet

DBT: The Six Levels of Validation

The "six levels of validation" is derived from DBT, Marsha Linehan's treatment modality for borderline personality disorder. This intervention is also useful for other types of personality disorders, such as those along the histrionic spectrum. Validation is a very important aspect of treatment and one that helps clients on the histrionic spectrum and others feel understood within their current life context.

Many individuals along the histrionic spectrum feel unheard, dismissed, and neglected by those they value most. Validating these clients, without providing approval of their maladaptive behaviors, can enhance the therapeutic relationship and assist in moving treatment forward by communicating acceptance and understanding in a very unambiguous manner. This is the central purpose of the six levels of validation.

Six Levels of Validation
1. Listen completely and with awareness
2. Accurately reflect your client's communication
3. Verbalize nonverbal emotions, thoughts, and behavior patterns
4. Identify historical factors that caused client's response
5. Empathize that the person's behavior is reasonable, meaningful, effective
6. Recognize him/her as someone with strengths and limitations

Next Steps

Following is a list of examples to clarify each of the six levels of validation. The exercise is designed to be used by you, the therapist, to gain better understanding of the different levels of validation and how to apply them. As you go over them, you may be surprised at the level you use most often and with which clients. I encourage you to enhance your skills in applying all six levels, as each has a time and place that can help move treatment forward and promote success.

After The DBT: Six Levels of Validation Exercise is the Feeling Connected and Understood Worksheet, which can be given to your client. This worksheet is intended to help both client and therapist gain better understanding of what makes the client feel heard; his or her emotions; his or her process of feeling, thinking, and behaving; and associated root causes. The worksheet also addresses standard response behaviors, meaning and purpose of past behavior, and strengths and weaknesses related to the client achieving his or her life goals. This is a powerful experience for many individuals and can help strengthen the therapeutic bond, as well as encourage therapeutic movement.

DBT: Six Levels of Validation

Level 1: Listen completely and with awareness (verbally and non-verbally).

"Tell me more about that."

"What was that like for you when …?"

"Will you paint a picture for me (verbally) of what that was like?"

Level 2: Accurately reflect your client's communication.

"You're angry that he did not call you the next day."

"It feels unfair that she would do that and get away with it, but you feel like you cannot."

"You feel lost when you try to connect to someone who does not feel that same way you do."

Level 3: Verbalize nonverbal emotions, thoughts, and behavior patterns.

"It is understandable that you would feel alone when she does not react the way you expect."

"Calling and hanging up several times a day provides you with certainty that she still exists and maybe provides you with a hope for reconciliation."

"You think no one will love you, and being intimate with many people provides you with some sort of love."

Level 4: Identify historical factors that caused the client's response.

"Your father storming out of the house when you got home late and him not coming back feeds your need for continual validation that someone you love is still there."

"Because your previous boss gave you a poor rating on your evaluation, it is understandable that you would be afraid to see your evaluation from your new boss."

"You have hurt yourself in the past, and this has provided you with the attention you feel you need."

Level 5: Empathize that the person's behavior is reasonable, meaningful, and effective.

"It makes sense to me to be afraid of your performance evaluation based on your past experience with being evaluated."

"You grew up in several foster homes, not knowing when you would be relocated to the next. I can certainly understand your wanting roots and a foundation in your life."

"Wanting to 'scream your head off' when you have to wait to get your needs met is understandable, since in the past this is the only thing that seemed to work with your mother."

Level 6: Recognize him or her as someone with strengths and limitations.

"As your therapist, it is hard for me to see you struggle and allow yourself to lose control when you accomplish so much when you're calm."

"You're a great artist with a deep imagination, and at times it is hard to separate the here-and-how from what is going on inside of you."

"Your loneliness takes over sometimes. You feel lonely and then call her, then judge yourself for doing so, knowing the pain that it is going to cause you. You have great insight, but your emotions and strong needs block access when you need it most."

Feeling Connected and Understood

Directions: The following questions are designed to identify what makes you feel heard and understood by someone else. Please be as honest as you can, and if you find some questions difficult to answer, bring this worksheet to your next session to explore with your therapist, or take time to really think about it.

What makes you feel heard by someone else?

_____

_____

_____

What is your "go-to" emotion (that first emotion that you tend to feel in situations that do not go as expected)? Some common ones are anger, sadness, gladness, loneliness, frustration, rejection, and fear.

_____

_____

_____

Fill in the following sequence:

When I feel (your "go-to" emotion or another)

⬇

I think (what thoughts first pop into your mind)

⬇

I do (in what behavior do you end up engaging)

Because of (add past experience) _____

_____

_____

_____

_____

Does the previous sequence (past experience influencing current behavior) make sense to you? If yes, please explain why you feel it is meaningful, reasonable, or understandable. This is not to explain yourself or to justify but to clarify your view. If not, how come?

_____

_____

_____

_____

List 3 weaknesses that prevent you from achieving your life goals:

1. _____

2. _____

3. _____

List 3 strengths you have to achieve your life goals:

1. _____

2. _____

3. _____

Dependent Versus Independent Action

It is not uncommon for the individual on the histrionic spectrum to have a stunted sense of independence. Most of his or her behavior is directed toward his or her sense of self and is founded on the attention and response the person gets from others. By acting in a more dependent and less independent manner, the client has difficulty developing a strong sense of self and self-confidence. In many cases, the individual on the histrionic spectrum lacks the initiative to make his or her own decisions, be alone, do what he or she wants, handle problems on his or her own, and speak up for himself or herself.

Next Steps

The following worksheet is designed to identify the degree to which the client engages in dependent and independent action related to various life circumstances and experiences.

It is exceptionally rare for any individual, particularly those along the histrionic spectrum, to be totally dependent or independent. The worksheet helps to illustrate what areas need to be developed and what areas need further examination to reach that healthy level of moderation within particular situations. In addition, the worksheet can help identify areas of strength to be used when the client feels that he or she is incapable of independent action.

Dependent Versus Independent Action

Directions: Use the following scale to compare your level of dependence versus independence in the various situations presented. Ask yourself how much input from someone else you require to make the decisions listed. There is no right or wrong answer, so please answer to the best of your ability. If you feel that a situation is not related to you, you may put "N/A" for "not applicable." When you are done, go over this with your therapist or on your own to assess if you tend to be more dependent or independent and in what situations.

Completely Dependent ←→ **Completely Independent**

0   1   2   3   4   5   6   7   8   9   10

Situation	Rating
Decide to go to a party	
Decide to quit your job	
Decide to change jobs	
Decide to end a relationship	
Decide to start a relationship	
Decide to become intimate with someone	
Decide to seek therapy	
Decide to end therapy	
Decide to not say anything	
Decide to react when angry	
Decide to lie	
Decide to be alone	
Decide to move to another state	
Decide to tell someone a secret	
Decide to forgive someone who has wronged you	
Decide to tell your employer what you think of him or her	
Decide to be unfaithful	
Decide to be friendly	
Decide to "just live with it"	
Decide to (write your own):	

Part Five
Borderline Personality Disorder Spectrum

Borderline Personality and Its Subtypes

Borderline personality disorder (BPD) is composed of "a pattern of instability in interpersonal relationships, self-image, and affects, and marked impulsivity," (APA, 2013, p. 645). BPD is "the most common personality disorder in clinical settings, and it is present in cultures around the world. However, this disorder is often incorrectly diagnosed or underdiagnosed in clinical practice," (Oldham et al., 2010). An incorrect BPD diagnosis is often given to clients who manifest traits similar to those of BPD but do not meet full criteria for the disorder. In many cases, these individuals actually fall along the borderline spectrum and can benefit from treatment directed at problematic behaviors and the core content that is driving these behaviors.

There are several components along the borderline spectrum:

Mild mood instability entails slight over-reactions to environmental triggers; individuals in this category are able to maintain control of themselves and objectively evaluate behavior and consequences. In socioeconomic settings, such as school, home, and work, the individual is often seen or referred to as "moody." He or she may cry easily, hold grudges longer than the average person, and require more energy from significant others and family members when he or she experiences emotional upsets.

The individual with mild mood instability is likely to have solid relationship boundaries and not sacrifice himself or herself for the good or pleasure of another. He or she may be emotionally sensitive but not emotionally vulnerable or likely to "wear his or her heart on his or her sleeve." A person who is on this end of the spectrum can self-soothe and rationally explore viable alternatives prior to acting out, which individuals who are further along the borderline spectrum are unable to do.

An individual who falls within the range of **lessening of self-control** along the borderline spectrum has all of the sensitivity of the person with mild mood instability but lacks the ability to regain control, self-soothe well, and realistically evaluate his or her environment accurately. A person within this range of the BPD spectrum is likely to have problems with friendships and romantic relationships. Erratic mood swings are common, and he or she may be misdiagnosed with bipolar disorder because bipolar disorder is also associated with changing mood states. However, there is always an identifiable trigger to the changes in mood for the person within the lessening of self-control region of the BPD spectrum, which is one of the key factors that differentiates individuals along the borderline spectrum from those with bipolar disorder (see Distinction Between Borderline Spectrum and Bipolar Disorder).

A person at the lessening of self-control point on the spectrum is likely to have difficulty maintaining long-term employment and academic commitments. Serial employment and/or poor school attendance is not uncommon because the person makes immediate decisions based on short-term situational triggers. Long-term stress is likely to move such an individual further along the borderline spectrum to **Histrionic Personality Disorder (HPD),** which has also been called "BPD light."

The greatest degree of overlap within Cluster B is between HPD and BPD, as both entail a tendency to be attention seeking, manipulative, and vacillating in emotions. However, the individual with BPD is more likely to have self-destructive and angry reactions in close relationships, as well as longstanding feelings of emptiness and disrupted identity.

Borderline personality disorder is an extensive, long-term, and inflexible pattern of maladaptive inner experiences and pathological outward behavior. It is composed of the following:

- **Feelings of abandonment**
- **Feelings of emptiness**
- **Unstable self-image**
- **High reactivity**
- **Intense relationships**
- **Self-mutilation**
- **Impulsivity**
- **Intense anger**
- **Dissociation**

Borderline Personality Disorder (BPD) is a complex disorder to treat, but also the most successfully treated of all the personality disorders. This workbook includes the most up-to-date treatment approaches to lessen session behaviors that thwart treatment progression.

Borderline Personality Spectrum

Individuals along the borderline spectrum often present with very complex histories and symptomatology. Individuals on the borderline spectrum tend to engage in behaviors and have experiences that justify how they see the world and function within it. Gathering data about past and present experiences can assist in identifying where your client is along the spectrum, as well as what obstacles he or she has overcome, what issues are continual, and the severity of these issues. The worksheet that follows can provide answers to many important questions for treatment, such as whether the intensity of particular past experiences has improved, worsened, or stayed the same.

The central components of the borderline spectrum include the following:

- Transient extreme emotions
- Extreme anxiety/depression
- Self-harming behavior
- Impulsive/risk taking behavior
- Inappropriate anger expressions
- Poor impulse control
- Emotional eating
- Suicidality
- Emptiness
- Unstable sense of identity

Next Steps

The Then and Now Experience Worksheet provides invaluable data for treatment, as it indicates the client's propensity for particular behaviors. It may indicate that your client has a history of self-harm but that he or she no longer engages in this behavior, for example. It is important to examine current and past behaviors in treatment, as well as what caused the individual to make the decision to cease a particular behavior or to continue it. Clients who are further along the borderline spectrum will rate the experiences listed with higher values. Use your client's responses to this worksheet to help identify strengths and coping strategies, as well as areas of weakness and difficulty that may be particularly stressful for him or her.

Then and Now Experience

Directions: Please complete the worksheet and rate the intensity of each experience from 0 to 10, with 0 being none at all/never happened and 10 being the most extreme experience you have ever had. Please be sure to share your results with your therapist.

Overwhelmed emotionally for a long time (days, weeks, months)

Past	0	1	2	3	4	5	6	7	8	9	10
Present	0	1	2	3	4	5	6	7	8	9	10

Overwhelmed emotionally for a short time (minutes, hours)

Past	0	1	2	3	4	5	6	7	8	9	10
Present	0	1	2	3	4	5	6	7	8	9	10

Extreme anxiety

Past	0	1	2	3	4	5	6	7	8	9	10
Present	0	1	2	3	4	5	6	7	8	9	10

Extreme depression

Past	0	1	2	3	4	5	6	7	8	9	10
Present	0	1	2	3	4	5	6	7	8	9	10

Cut, burnt, hit, or banged head to harm self

Past	0	1	2	3	4	5	6	7	8	9	10
Present	0	1	2	3	4	5	6	7	8	9	10

Impulsive/risky behavior (e.g., risky driving, unsafe sex, gambling sprees, taking illicit drugs)

Past	0	1	2	3	4	5	6	7	8	9	10
Present	0	1	2	3	4	5	6	7	8	9	10

Inappropriate expressions of anger (e.g., physical confrontations, verbal aggression)

Past	0	1	2	3	4	5	6	7	8	9	10
Present	0	1	2	3	4	5	6	7	8	9	10

Difficulty controlling impulses

Past	0	1	2	3	4	5	6	7	8	9	10
Present	0	1	2	3	4	5	6	7	8	9	10

Emotional eating (e.g., binging, purging, anorexia, bulimia)

Past	0	1	2	3	4	5	6	7	8	9	10
Present	0	1	2	3	4	5	6	7	8	9	10

Suicidal thoughts

Past	0	1	2	3	4	5	6	7	8	9	10
Present	0	1	2	3	4	5	6	7	8	9	10

Suicide attempts

Past	0	1	2	3	4	5	6	7	8	9	10
Present	0	1	2	3	4	5	6	7	8	9	10

Fear of being alone

Past	0	1	2	3	4	5	6	7	8	9	10
Present	0	1	2	3	4	5	6	7	8	9	10

Uncertainty of who or what you are (self-image)

Past	0	1	2	3	4	5	6	7	8	9	10
Present	0	1	2	3	4	5	6	7	8	9	10

Distinction Between Borderline Spectrum and Bipolar Disorder

There is often difficulty in discerning between the pathology shown in clients along the borderline spectrum and those with bipolar disorder. It has been found that there is substantial diagnostic overlap between bipolar disorder and BPD due to the inherent complexity of presentation and shared features (Deltito et al., 2001; MacKinnon & Pies, 2006). A study of 100 adults from the Bipolar Disorder Research Program of the Payne Whitney Clinic in New York found that onset of bipolar disorder was prior to age 19 in 55% of the participants, onset of first depressive episode was before age 19 in 56%, and first manic or hypomanic episode was before age 19 in 44% (Goldberg & Garno, 2009). Findings showed that early onset of bipolar disorder increased the probability of a BPD diagnosis.

Next Steps

The following checklist is composed of discernible characteristics between BPD and bipolar disorder. If you are uncertain about which disorder best fits your client, go through the nine characteristics listed and note whether they are present or absent. Compare your results with the identified characteristics in the table that follows the checklist. It is possible for your client to meet criteria for both disorders. In these cases, it is always best to get the bipolar disorder under control before attempting to work with the borderline spectrum or personality disorder traits.

Distinction Between Borderline Spectrum and Bipolar Disorder

Directions: In the first checklist, mark the characteristics present in your client. Then, use the answer key in Appendix A to help determine which disorder is present. This is not a comprehensive tool to diagnose borderline personality disorder or bipolar disorder but rather, a tool to help discern between the two.

Present	Absent	Characteristic
		Intensive efforts to avoid being alone
		Pattern of unstable/intense interpersonal relationships
		Disturbance in core self and self-identity
		Recurrent suicidal behavior, threats, or gestures, or self-mutilating behavior in response to stressor or end of relationship.
		Mood episodes are more discrete and longer acting and can often present without any obvious trigger
		Symptoms present in episodes that are a change from the person's typical behavior
		Impulsivity is only seen during a period of elevated mood, hypomanic or manic (without identifiable trigger)
		Paranoia or dissociation is short lived, without the development of long-term delusions or hallucinations
		Delusions and hallucinations are present only during a depressed, manic, or mixed episode

Lessening Self-Mutilation

Self-mutilation is a complex byproduct of a wide variety of mental illnesses. It has been associated with substance abuse, eating disorders, posttraumatic stress disorder, major depressive disorder, anxiety disorders, schizophrenia, and BPD (Klonsky et al., 2003). It can be defined as the infliction of harm on the self without intent to end one's life. Klonsky and colleagues found that 4% of the general population and between 14 and 35% of college students have engaged in some form of self-mutilation, such as cutting (70%), banging or hitting themselves (21–44%), and burning themselves (15–35%). The researchers also found no conclusive evidence to show that one gender engages in self-harm at a higher rate than another.

Benjamin has defined a sequence of symptoms leading up to and following self-mutilation by borderline clients. The six steps in the sequence are listed below:

The first step in the sequence entails the person being devalued by an identified important other. These feelings become internalized, and the individual withdraws and begins to disconnect from his or her feelings and internal subjective state. He or she turns on the self, internalizing the identified other's view, and then engages in self-mutilation/self-sabotaging behaviors that provide relief. Relief is not the singular subjective state of lessening anxiety but takes on many forms. Various definitions of relief listed below have been reported by clients on the borderline spectrum to explain why they harm themselves:

- **To make anguish known to others**

- **To get revenge on an identified other**

- **To force someone else to demonstrate a caring act**

- **To reduce anxiety**

- **To treat myself the way the internalized other wants me to be treated**

- **To end an argument**

- **To punish perceived "bad self"**

- **To relieve numbness (to feel something)**

If the final component of relief was not present, it is doubtful that the individual would continually participate in the self-harming behavior(s).

Next Steps

The worksheet that follows is meant to help the client identify his or her thoughts and feelings associated with each step in the sequence. The therapist can use the person's responses to gain understanding and to disrupt the sequence that leads to self-mutilation.

If the therapist can work with the client in disrupting the self-harm/self-sabotage sequence, it should lessen the probability of him or her engaging in this behavior.

Six Steps in the
Self-Mutilation Sequence

Directions: Please answer each of the questions below as honestly as you can. The goal of this worksheet is to help you gain insight and understanding into your tendency to harm yourself and to help you get control of this behavior.

1. **Who has hurt you, either physically, sexually, or emotionally?**

    _____

    _____

2. **From whom do you physically withdraw when the person(s) identified in #1 hurts you?**

    _____

3. **Describe what it feels like to detach from yourself.** (Some people report that they feel themselves disconnect from their emotions, body, and reality.)

    _____

    _____

    _____

4. **How do you feel about yourself when the person(s) identified in #1 hurts you and you are detached from yourself?**

    _____

    _____

    _____

5. **What is the first thought you have about how to harm yourself? How do you think about doing it, and then how do you actually do it?** (For some individuals this is different.)

    _____

    _____

    _____

6. **What do you get out of hurting yourself?** (This can be internal and/or external.)

    _____

    _____

    _____

Some individuals prefer to draw what their detachment is like. If you prefer to draw instead of or in addition to describing your detachment, please use the space provided here:

Attachment and the Borderline Spectrum

Individuals along the borderline spectrum are likely to have difficulty genuinely attaching in the therapeutic relationship. Treating attachment issues is a complex process and involves identifying and working with the insecure attachment pattern and recreating a more secure attachment in its place. The therapeutic environment and relationship are ideal for doing this, but improvements in attachment security will wax and wane throughout the therapeutic process. This process is similar to what occurs when a small child first ventures out onto a playground: he or she steps away from the attachment figure, testing the environment, and then returns to the attachment figure to find security. In treatment, the client on the borderline spectrum will move toward and away from the therapist, as well as idealize then devalue the therapist's worth.

To examine attachment and the borderline spectrum, we use the model devised by Bartholomew and Horowitz shown here:

	Positive View of Self	**Negative View of Self**
Positive View of Others	**Secure Attachment** Hopeful Satisfied Trusting Self-Disclosing	**Preoccupied Attachment** Hopeless Dissatisfied Trusting Self-Disclosing
Negative View of Others	**Dismissing Attachment** Hopeful Satisfied Distrusting Non-Disclosing	**Fearful Attachment** Hopeless Dissatisfied Distrusting Non-Disclosing

Bowlby's attachment theory fits neatly into the borderline spectrum framework. Several studies have found a link between attachment and early separation, which contributes to distorted internal working models that affect one's ability to predict, understand, process, and adjust to responses and reactions from significant others. (For more information, see Fox, 2013.)

The individual along the borderline spectrum has a preoccupied attachment style. Individuals with this sort of attachment tend to view others as positive and themselves as negative. Other indications of a preoccupied attachment style include the tendency to fall into distress, experience poor emotional control, and express symptomatology aimed at the self. Preoccupied individuals also tend to experience the vacillating view that others will save them. Due to the view that others are good and the self is bad, the individual on the borderline spectrum tends to be vulnerable, relationship seeking, and highly sensitive to rejection. These behaviors and feelings manifest quickly in the therapeutic relationship.

Next Steps

The History of Self and Other Worksheet is designed to elicit responses related to attachment and how the individual on the borderline spectrum perceives and manages attachment disruptions. The further along the spectrum he or she is, the more difficulty he or she may have in responding, as the worksheet relates directly to the core issues of the preoccupied attachment style, such as the tendency to be cautious in connecting to others through idealization and devaluation.

The initial part of the worksheet addresses several salient aspects of the individual's upbringing and helps him or her identify his or her perception of those important objects. The latter part of the worksheet compares the child self with the current self; explores the model of relationships, loneliness, and success; and challenges the client to think about how to "do it differently" to break the patterns of preoccupied attachment. There is also a section in which the person can draw the child self and the current self. This worksheet can assist in working through many of the core attachment issues individuals on the borderline spectrum need to rectify to move forward and gain control of and overcome their pathology.

Ask your client to fill out the worksheet, and discuss the answers in a very open and non-threatening manner. The client will be highly sensitive to feedback if he or she answered honestly; this is contingent on the strength of your relationship. The stronger the relationship, the more honest the responses are likely to be. Remember that every answer is a valuable one. If your client gives an answer that you know is false, that still provides useful data in treatment. All information, even a lie, is fodder for treatment. Your client's answers can be seen as a projective.

History of Self and Other

Directions: Please complete the following sentences.

I would describe my childhood as _____

_____

_____

_____

The person I felt closest to growing up was _____

_____

_____

_____

The person I wanted to be closest to while I was growing up was _____

_____

_____

_____

The person who brought me the most pain growing up was _____

_____

_____

_____

I often felt helpless while I was growing up when I was around _____

_____

_____

_____

When I was a child, if I asserted myself my loved one often _____
_____
_____
_____

I know my adult self is different from my child self because _____
_____
_____
_____

I know my adult self is the same as my child self because _____
_____
_____
_____

I model my current relationships on my relationship with _____
_____
_____
_____

When I am alone, it makes me feel _____
_____
_____
_____

When I am close to succeeding, it makes me feel _____
_____
_____
_____

The best way for me to "do it differently" is to _____
_____
_____
_____

Directions: Use this space to draw yourself as a child and how you see yourself now:

Child Self	Current Self

Identifying the Transitional Object

A study that explored BPD and attachment to transitional objects, such as stuffed animals, was conducted by Hooley and Wilson-Murphy with a nonclinical sample of 80 adults (61 females and 19 males). Results showed the most intense attachment to transitional objects in borderline participants. In addition, those with intense attachments to transitional objects reported less parental care, caregivers who were more controlling, greater relationship anxiety, and more childhood trauma experiences. Attachment to these transitional objects may have served as a substitution for attachment needs that were not met early on and illustrated the participants' desire for connection and the emotional inability to obtain it.

It is very important to identify the transitional or comfort object in your client's life. This can be anything, such as a stuffed animal, a Matchbox car, a "security blanket," or even a pet. It is imperative that you have a solid foundation in your therapeutic relationship and that your client has a sense of comfort when you bring up the concept of a transitional object. Without the foundational relationship, your client is unlikely to tell you what his or her transitional object is and what it means to him or her. He or she may not recognize it as a transitional object but as an "antique" or a "favorite childhood toy I've just always hung on to."

If the transitional object is a pet, it is important to recognize that pets die, and this loss can cause further problems down the road for your client on the borderline spectrum. In these cases, a useful strategy is to move the value of the transitional object to something related to the pet that is tangible (e.g., the pet's collar). This provides something of value for the client to hold on to when the living transitional object does pass away.

Next Steps

The Transitional Object Worksheet is designed to help you work with your client to identify the meaning of his or her transitional object and what it represents. Discussing and bringing in the transitional object (I have had clients bring in stuffed and living animals for one session) can help the therapist connect with the client on a deeper level and show trust as the client shares his or her very personal and private feelings about this comfort object. This intervention can be used at difficult times, such as when the client is devaluing himself or herself or the therapist. During a particularly difficult session, I asked my client how her teddy bear (transitional object), Maroon, would feel about her hurting herself, as she devalued me at this point in our treatment. The client decided that Maroon did not want her to hurt herself, and we discussed how this could help to prevent my client from future self-harm.

Transitional Object

Directions: The questions that follow pertain to your transitional or comfort object. A transitional or comfort object is something you use to obtain comfort and security while you are away from a secure base (e.g., trusting other or caregiver). This can be a stuffed animal, security blanket, Matchbox car, or anything you hold dear. It cannot be another person or a body part.

What it the most valued object in your life?

_____

_____

What makes this so special to you?

_____

_____

What/who does it represent?

_____

_____

How has it changed over the years?

_____

_____

How do you feel when you hold your object?

_____

_____

What would this object say about you if asked how you have changed since it came into your life?

_____

_____

What opinion would this object have about you?

_____

_____

How does this object help you?

_____

_____

Concept of "IT"

The concept of "IT" is a very powerful technique to amplify the true self of the client on the borderline spectrum, while minimizing his or her false self. This intervention is best used with a client whose true self is kind, caring, and positive and whose false self is composed of malice, anger, rage, and other "negative" components. This technique is useful with clients on the histrionic and narcissistic spectra as well. The object of this exercise is to first identify the false self, "IT," which tends to be much larger and easier to identify than the true self. This is because "IT" has been in place and often encouraged for so long that it has overshadowed the true self such that the individual only, or mostly, operates from his or her false self. These individuals may not be sure what their true self is.

Next Steps

Two examples of this exercise follow. The first (Concept of "IT" Worksheet 1) is to be used earlier in treatment to identify what components promote or occupy the false self, "IT," and the true self. The second (Concept of "IT" Worksheet 2) is to be used at the conclusion of treatment. You can see that through treatment, "IT" is significantly diminished, while the true self is encouraged to grow and overshadow the false self. The example provided is from one of my clients on the borderline spectrum. In treatment, she and I examined how the presentation of "IT" and the minimization of the true self were a method of safeguarding her from being hurt. In reality, however, the client still got hurt and often was hurt more when operating from "IT."

Through the course of treatment with this particular client, she and I would continually go back to talking about her false self and true self and examine which she was utilizing in certain situations. For example, this client physically attacked another woman while trying to get into a checkout line at the supermarket because the other woman got in line ahead of her "when she knew I was heading for the shortest line." The fight was broken up by store employees, and the client was charged with assault. When I met with this client, I asked her, "What motivated this behavior, 'IT' or your true self?" She lowered her head, embarrassed, and replied, "IT." We then processed how her true self would have managed this situation (see how this is not a justification for behavior below). We would do this multiple times through our treatment time together, which was more than 2 years.

If this powerful technique is used, it should *NEVER* be forgotten. Furthermore, the concept of "IT" should not be given a proper name: We want to discourage naming "IT" because ideally, we want to eventually minimize "IT" and throw "IT" away. It is the same reason you do not name a dog or cat you are not going to keep; giving something a name creates an attachment to it.

This technique should never be seen as a justification for bad behavior. The individual will still have to take responsibility for his or her behavior and its consequences regardless of whether he or she is operating from "IT" or his or her true self. The lesson we are trying to highlight is that acting in accordance with the values of the true self increases the probability of positive outcomes, whereas acting from "IT" increases the probability of negative outcomes.

Concept of "IT"

This example shows a client's responses when her false self, "IT," is more prominent and controlling than her true self. This client operates almost 100% of each day using her false self, "IT." This is when she interacts with friends, family, coworkers, and significant others. The object of the exercise is to reduce the behaviors associated with "IT" and enhance the true self. This is done through your recognizing who has control and being patient with yourself and in your decisions. The Concept of "IT" is *NEVER* a justification for bad behavior; it is a conceptualization of how you see yourself and what drives your behavior. See the next page for how the Concept of "IT" might look at the end of treatment.

False Self, "IT"　　　　　　　　　**True Self**

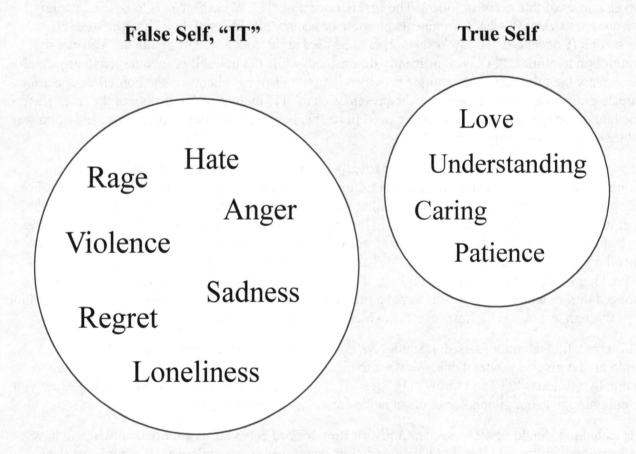

Concept of "IT"

The example below shows a client's responses at the end of treatment reevaluating the concept of "IT." The false self is still there, those issues remain, but they are not controlling the client any longer. The true self has taken over and the individual is more authentic with important people in his or her life and is creating a positive influence on those around him or her.

False Self, "IT"

Hate
Rage
Anger
Violence
Regret
Sadness
Loneliness

True Self

Love
Patience
Caring
Self -Worth
Understanding
Self -Control

Concept of "IT"

Directions: Use the space that follows to draw your concept of your true self and your false self, or "IT." Write what each is composed of and what aspects cause it to motivate you. It may take time to discern what your true self is and what your false self, "IT," has become over many years of various experiences. Be patient with yourself and know that there are no wrong answers.

False Self, "IT"	True Self

Motivations and Triggers

Most individuals along the borderline spectrum have difficulty identifying their motivations and triggers and managing stressful situations. Often, such clients will respond to situations in haste, which significantly increases the probability of an adverse outcome. The Motivations and Triggers Worksheet, which follows, is designed to help the client walk through a stressful situation and encourages insight into emotional and/or thought-based triggers he or she is likely to use. It also assists the client in identifying alternative methods and coping strategies to better manage the intense and stressful situation and asks him or her to identify what he or she thinks and feels about the alternative. Many clients on the borderline spectrum do not slow down and consider whether their triggers are emotional or thought based and how vivid their images of intense and stressful situations actually are, which tends to cause them to act out too quickly remove the dissonant stimuli.

Next Steps

The worksheet identifies and encourages the development of both emotional and thought content to increase the probability of identifying salient and useable alternatives to adverse behavior, imagery, thoughts, and emotions that are very common in clients along the borderline spectrum.

Motivations and Triggers

Directions: This worksheet is designed to help you walk through a past or present stressful situation, identify your thoughts and reactions, and devise the best way to manage such situations.

Describe a stressful situation, perhaps one from your past or one you are dealing with right now:

_____

_____

_____

_____

What is your typical response in this stressful situation?

_____

_____

_____

Circle what is more of a trigger for you:

                    Thoughts   Emotions

What is the first thought that goes through you mind when you think about this situation?

_____

_____

_____

What is the first emotion you feel when you think about this situation?

_____

_____

What is the first image in your mind when you think about this situation?

_____

_____

_____

_____

How intense and vivid is this imagery (0 = not at all; 10 = intense and vivid)

0   1   2   3   4   5   6   7   8   9   10

In your mind, how do you see the situation resolving as a result of your behavior?

_____

_____

_____

Can you think of another way to better manage this situation?

_____

_____

Circle which of the following coping strategies you could employ to have greater control over your motivations, triggers, and the environment when dealing with this situation or one like it.

Use humor (not sarcasm)	Exercise
Seek support	Adjust expectations
Problem solve	Vent (verbal/written note to self)
Use relaxation techniques	Play a video game or watch TV

How can you employ one or more of the coping strategies listed previously?

_____

_____

What do you think the situation would be like if you were to use the coping strategies and/or the new approach listed previously?

_____

_____

How would the situation feel for you using the coping strategies and/or the new approach listed previously?

_____

_____

_____

Identifying Maladaptive Patterns

When working with individuals along the borderline spectrum, it is important to get them to recognize their adaptive and maladaptive patterns of behavior. Most individuals have a few adaptive patterns, but their maladaptive patterns tend to be so fixed that using them is second nature and often immediately reinforcing. Such maladaptive patterns can include unhealthy roles, drug and alcohol abuse, and promiscuity. By the time these individuals enter treatment, they are hopefully ready to change these patterns. Benjamin (1996) outlines five categories of responses that can be helpful to use when working with individuals with personality disorders and those along the borderline spectrum. These include the following:

> 1. Facilitating collaboration
>
> 2. Facilitating pattern recognition
>
> 3. Blocking maladaptive patterns
>
> 4. Strengthening the will to give up maladaptive patterns
>
> 5. Facilitating new learning

Next Steps

The Maladaptive Patterns Worksheet is a tool for exploring Categories 2 and 3. The first part of the worksheet is designed to help the client identify his or her maladaptive pattern (#2) and block the maladaptive pattern (#3) by applying a more helpful and adaptive pattern of functioning. Categories 4 and 5 are addressed throughout the remainder of this workbook. For the Maladaptive Patterns worksheet, the client is encouraged to use the adaptive methods of functioning, outlined in the second part of the worksheet, at all times and not only during times of stress or disappointment.

This worksheet is highly useful in treatment as it helps to identify new adaptive patterns that the client is willing to utilize. There are 25 maladaptive patterns and 50 adaptive patterns listed. This is done intentionally to illustrate that there are more positive and adaptive patterns than maladaptive ones from which to choose.

Maladaptive Patterns

Directions: The following is a list of the 25 most common maladaptive patterns. Please put a check (✓) next to all that you have engaged in and tend to use after encountering a setback, failure, or other stressful event in your life.

	Compliant surrendering (giving in quietly)
	"Being accepting of the punitive partner/parent"
	Overcompensating
	Being the punitive partner/parent (believing you should be punished for "bad self")
	Being the demanding partner/parent (the "right" way to be is to be perfect)
	Abusing alcohol or recreational drugs
	Using avoidance
	Procrastinating
	Overeating
	Undereating
	Self-injuring
	Spending excessively
	Engaging in unprotected or impulsive sexual behavior
	Withdrawing from positive influences
	Oversleeping
	Undersleeping

	Filling up every minute of the day to avoid facing problems
	Taking out your stress on others (lashing out, angry outbursts, physical violence)
	Beating yourself up mentally
	Misusing prescription drugs, not taking them as prescribed/instructed
	Denying the problem exists
	Engaging in addictive behaviors, such as gambling, internet addiction, sexual addiction, thrill seeking or taking unnecessary risks, or any activity done to excess
	Burning bridges, as in cutting off friendships and other relationships, quitting jobs, and moving frequently
	Denying yourself playtime, rest, social interaction, fun, and other healthy human needs
	Dissociating (detaching from the present to avoid emotional distress)

Many people feel that they get a great benefit out of their maladaptive pattern(s); otherwise, they would not engage in it/them. Can you describe what you get out of using your maladaptive pattern(s)?

_____

_____

Do you want to give up your maladaptive pattern(s)?   Yes   No

If you want to give up your maladaptive pattern(s), which of the following 50 adaptive patterns could you use instead? (Put a check [✓] next to all that apply.)

	Exercise (e.g., running, walking)		Spending time with friends
	Writing (poetry, stories, journal)		Scribbling/doodling
	Do a word search or crossword puzzle		Watching a favorite TV show or movie
	Posting on Internet forums and answering others' posts		Playing a musical instrument
	Painting your nails, doing your make-up or hair		Singing
	Cloud or sky watching		Hitting a punching bag

	Covering yourself with Band-Aids where you want to cut		Letting yourself cry
	Taking a nap		Taking a hot shower or relaxing bath
	Playing with a pet		Going shopping
	Cleaning something		Knitting or sewing
	Reading a good book		Listening to music
	Meditating		Using aromatherapy (candle, lotion, room spray)
	Going somewhere public		Playing video/computer games
	Ripping paper into tiny pieces		Playing basketball or shooting hoops
	Baking cookies		Alphabetizing your music/DVDs/books
	Painting or drawing		Writing a letter or an email (whether or not to send)
	Hugging a pillow or stuffed animal		Studying something up close, like a rock or your hand
	Dancing		Searching online for new songs/artists
	Teaching your pet a new trick		Moving EVERYTHING in your room to a new spot
	Getting together with friends		Playing with modeling clay or Play-Doh
	Playing Frisbee, soccer, or catch		Doing yoga
	Completing something you've been putting off		"Shopping" online (without buying anything)
	Taking up a new hobby		Looking up recipes, cooking a meal
	Looking at pretty things like flowers or art		Creating or building something
	Praying		Making a list of blessings in your life

Remember to use these adaptive patterns as much as you can and not just under stressful circumstances. Make them a part of your life so that when you do encounter stress you have more positives "to fall back on."

Copyright 2015 © Daniel J. Fox • *Antisocial, Borderline, Narcissistic & Histrionic Workbook* • All Rights Reserved

165

Unconscious Wishes and Fears

Giving up unconscious wishes and fears requires that a client let go of those internalized destructive dreams, wishes, and hopes that his or her maladaptive patterns will produce positive outcomes. For example, is your client on the borderline spectrum willing to give up using alcohol and drugs and instead try interacting with people in an honest and sober manner? Underlying this maladaptive pattern is the protective wish that the client "can only be myself when I am drunk," so that if he or she is rejected or has an adverse outcome, he or she can defer responsibility to the alcohol or drugs. If he or she is sober, he or she cannot—all he or she has left is fear.

Next Steps

The worksheets that follow are guides to discovering the unconscious wishes and fears of your client along the borderline or other personality disorder spectrum. The first worksheet asks the client to identify his or her wish, associated fear, and the behavior in which he or she engages to achieve that wish or avoid that fear. The client is then asked to operationally define how he or she knows when he or she is being motivated by the fear and when he or she has achieved the wish. The second worksheet asks the client to draw himself or herself when he or she is consumed by the wish or fear. This gives the therapist good insight into imagery being used by the client and how he or she sees himself or herself in the midst of his or her wish and fear.

Your client should be encouraged to complete the worksheets, and you, the therapist, should be his or her cheerleader in the attempt. This is not an easy conceptualization, and most clients on the borderline spectrum prefer not to know their unconscious wishes and fears but instead to simply act on them. Long-term change requires unsettling these wishes and fears and gaining control over them, and these worksheets, in concert with the therapeutic process, will help your client to do just that.

Unconscious Wishes and Fears

Directions: Please complete the sentences regarding what you wish to achieve in your life, what you fear will happen if you are authentic, what behaviors are motivated by your wish or your fear (you are welcome to include both if you would like), and what identifiers you see in you and your life that indicate that you are being motivated by your fear or that you have gotten your wish.

I wish: _____

_____

_____

I fear: _____

_____

_____

I do: _____ because I WISH/FEAR (circle one): _____

_____

_____

I will know I am being motivated by my fear when: _____

_____

_____

I am false or fake to get my wish because I: _____

_____

_____

My fear is not stronger than me because: _____

_____

_____

I will know I have gotten my wish when: _____

_____

_____

A more authentic approach to getting my wish would be to: _____

_____

_____

Pictorial Wish and Fear

Directions: Please use the space below to draw how you see yourself consumed by your wish and your fear.

My Fear	My Wish

Part Six
Dialectical Behavioral Therapy Worksheets

Dialectical Behavioral Therapy Worksheets

This section reviews the four central components of Dialectical and Behavior Therapy (DBT), which was created by Marsha Linehan: mindfulness, interpersonal effectiveness, emotion regulation, and distress tolerance. These four components are critical in influencing client change and helping clients approach life in a more managed and healthy way. DBT is designed to be support oriented, cognitively based, and effective with your most difficult clients. In this section, there are five worksheets corresponding to each of the four components, and these are designed to assist in the growth and development of emotional, behavioral, and overall well-being while lessening personality disorder spectrum pathology in your clients. Many frontline clinicians do not have the time or resources to complete the extensive DBT program, but even parts of the program, such as the worksheets included in this workbook, can help clients build essential skills and attenuate problems related to personality disorders.

Mindfulness is a core component of DBT. Mindfulness skills are to be the first skills taught and comprise psychological and behavioral skills, including meditation. The worksheets presented here will help your clients gain mastery of these invaluable skills as they learn to observe, describe, and participate in the present without reacting. They will also help clients gain a better understanding of their feelings in the moment and help them stay present.

Interpersonal Effectiveness is aimed at building social potency within a wide variety of contexts. Interpersonal effectiveness is based on changing automatic behaviors that are typically triggered by repeated situations and works to develop new responses or add a greater variety of possible responses when difficult situations arise. Assertiveness and problem-solving skills are central to getting one's needs met in a productive and healthy manner. The included worksheets address critical concepts to help clients authentically interact with the people in their life by building healthy relationships and moving away from unhealthy ones. Clients are also taught how to balance "wants and shoulds," as well as several other key strategies.

Emotion Regulation entails managing intense and labile mood states often seen in individuals along the personality disorder spectrum. Although Linehan's therapy was developed for BPD, it has been found to be useful with other individuals along the different personality disorder spectra. Emotion regulation is aimed at assisting the client in managing painful emotions that encourage or exacerbate acting out and other inappropriate behaviors. Worksheets included in this section include those that address identifying and working with primary and secondary emotions, replacing negative emotions, identifying painful emotions, and enhancing the ability to cope in stressful situations.

Distress Tolerance skills are designed to help the individual learn to manage painful circumstances and emotions in a more effective manner. The client is taught the skills of tolerating and accepting emotional discomfort as part of a normal and healthy life and coming to terms with change and how to "do it differently." If these skills are not learned, clients on the borderline and other personality disorder spectra will continually be wedded to immediate reactions that thwart healthy change and growth.

Mindfulness

The practice of being
fully aware and present
in the moment

Observe, Describe, Participate

The three main components of mindfulness are *observe*, *describe*, and *participate*. *Observe* is the ability to experience circumstances without allowing judgments to color the experience. *Describe* refers to the skills necessary to actively put words to the experience. *Participate* is to actively and consciously be present in whatever is happening in life, not just see or understand it. Each of these is described in the following worksheet, which is to be given to your client to allow him or her to practice.

Mindfulness is like any skill: the more you use it, the better you get at it. The key is to practice mindfulness every day and not just "try it" during times of stress. If your client only uses mindfulness when stressed, he or she will not find the usefulness in it and will not have built up the skills to counter and overcome significant stress. This is the central reason why Linehan recommends that mindfulness be learned first when using DBT. If you approach a problem from a stance of mindfulness, you can control and engage the situation in a more efficacious manner. When clients along the borderline or other personality disorder spectrum approach problems from intense emotional viewpoints and motivations, they tend to have a greater probability of negative outcomes. Mindfulness can be the key to starting your client on a path to overcoming his or her emotional burdens and learning even more helpful skills to create a positive future.

Observe, Describe, Participate

Directions: In this exercise, the three central components of mindfulness and how to use them are described. For people who have not used these skills before, they are invaluable and can contribute to significant life change. The key is to practice them every day and incorporate them into your daily routine.

OBSERVE

1. Just notice where you are right now.
2. See how long your feeling lasts.
3. Think of a "SLIPPERY EEL": Thoughts, feelings, and emotions just slide off as they enter your mind.
4. Only notice your senses—touch, feel, smell, taste, and hear.
5. MASTER your ATTENTION and focus, but do not hold onto or dismiss anything.

DESCRIBE

1. Use words to describe your experience.
2. Just give the "facts"—a THOUGHT is just a thought, and a FEELING is just a feeling.
3. Use words with which everyone agrees.
4. Do not get caught in content.
5. Let go of being "right" or "wrong"—emotions are neither.

PARTICIPATE

1. Get caught in the FLOW, or in the ZONE, of your experience.
2. Follow your INTUITION.
3. Be one with your experience.
4. Allow yourself to be NATURAL in the situation.
5. PRACTICE, PRACTICE, PRACTICE so these skills become a part of you.

Feel the Moment

The mindfulness Feel the Moment Worksheet is meant to help your client work through a current emotional state, build confidence in overcoming it, and identify its root once he or she is in a calm and present state of mind. Your client will first identify his or her current adverse emotional state, then rate it. Next, he or she will connect it to the past when he or she overcame similar emotions and rate his or her current emotional state again. Next, he or she is to bring his or her mind forward to the present and let go of past and future thoughts and feelings and then rate his or her emotional state. Lastly, the client will describe what made him or her uncomfortable and describe his or her current level of discomfort. Through mindfulness, your clients develop a sense of a deeper connection to themselves and the outside world.

Next Steps

Give the following worksheet to your client and have him or her fill it out. The more he or she completes this worksheet, the greater the skill development. Go over the results with your client. You are likely to see a decline in the emotional rating as he or she moves through the exercise.

Feel the Moment

Directions: Go through each of the steps below to help you manage stressful situations.

Rate your level of discomfort
from 0 = none to 10 = most intense

Close your eyes and get in touch with some current discomfort or anxiety—one that you are experiencing right now.

Remember that you have had to get through such feelings in the past

Now refocus on the present—let go of all the past and future thoughts and feelings.

Write in the box below what made you uncomfortable and try to describe your level of discomfort

Ready, Breathe, Draw

Directions: Do this exercise as often as you would like to help calm yourself and bring yourself to awareness. It is like any skill—the more you do it, the better you get at it. THIS IS NOT ABOUT ARTISTIC ABILITY. Find an object in the room you are in or in your mind's eye. Take a moment and think about the major and minor details of this object, allowing other thoughts to slide in and out of your mind. Breathe slowly and deeply as you do this, noticing if the object is big or small, wood or metal, old or new. Grab any writing utensil you like. (Some people like to have a special mindfulness pen or pencil given to them by their therapist or by a friend just for this exercise.) Use the space below to draw this object to the best of your ability.

Ready ... Breathe ... Draw

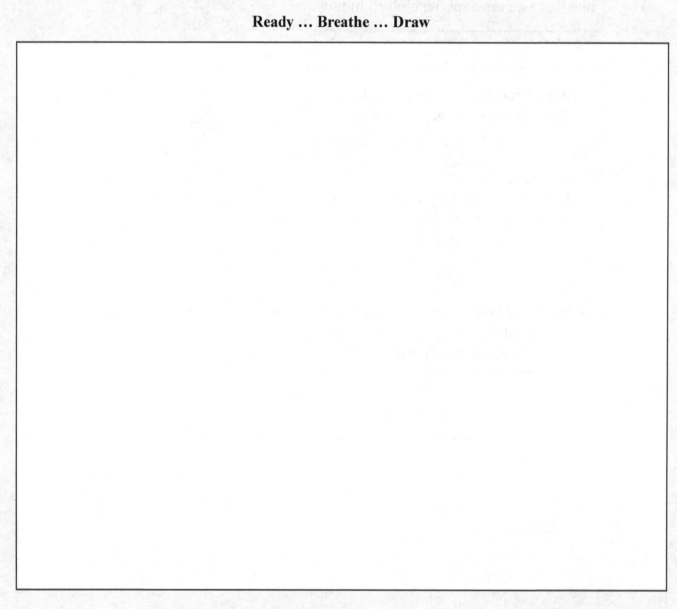

Let It Melt (Chocolate!!!)

Directions: This exercise does not have to be done with chocolate. (But Hershey's Kisses® are effective and fun!) It can be effective with ice cubes, peppermints, or anything that takes time to dissolve.

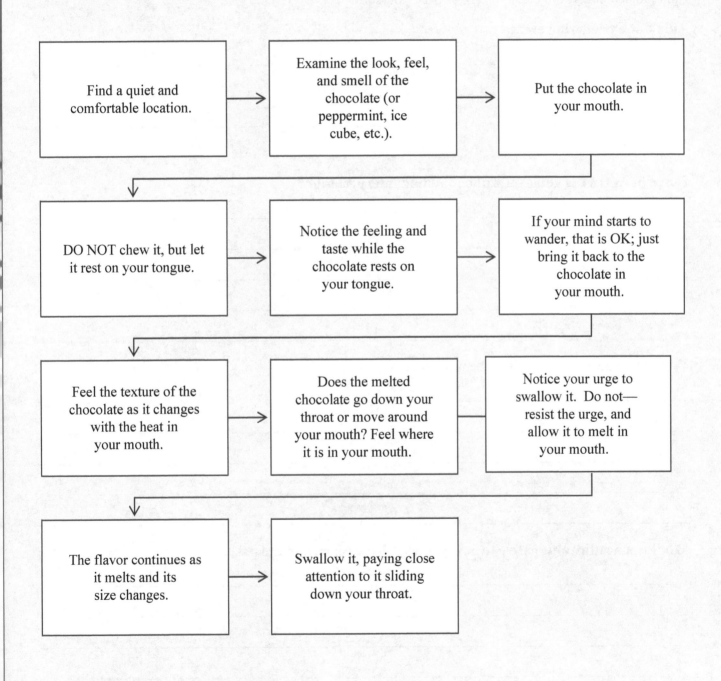

Participating to Do It Differently

Directions: Follow the steps listed here to help strengthen your non-judgmental approach to situations you experience in life. Do not be concerned with what is "right" or "wrong." Instead, let go of "being right" to achieve your goal and learn to trust yourself.

Think of a triggering event:

_____

_____

_____

_____

Describe WHAT is going on without adding interpretation:

_____

_____

_____

_____

_____

What can you do to ACCEPT the moment?

_____

_____

_____

_____

What is a healthy alternative to how you may have reacted in the past?

_____

_____

_____

_____

_____

Steps to Mindfulness

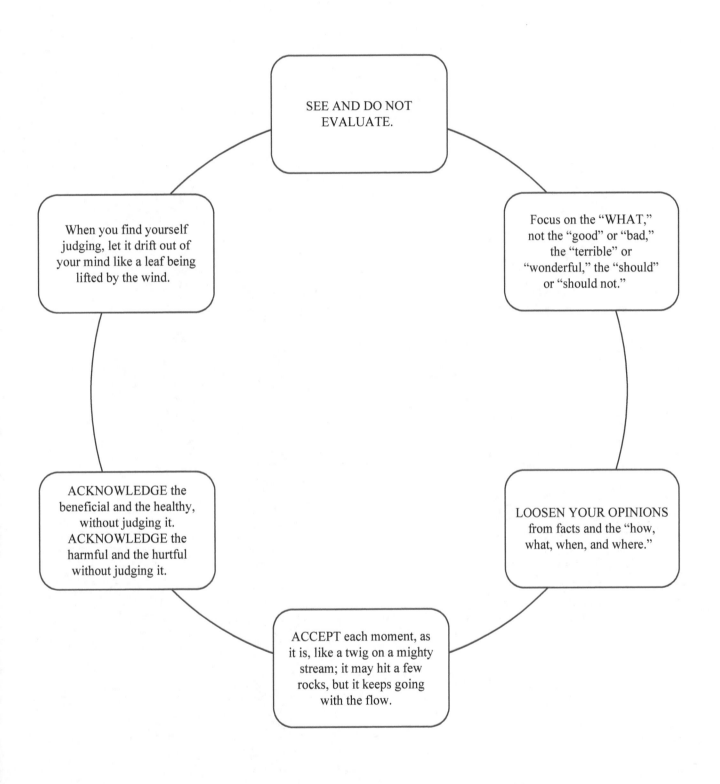

SEE AND DO NOT EVALUATE.

Focus on the "WHAT," not the "good" or "bad," the "terrible" or "wonderful," the "should" or "should not."

LOOSEN YOUR OPINIONS from facts and the "how, what, when, and where."

ACCEPT each moment, as it is, like a twig on a mighty stream; it may hit a few rocks, but it keeps going with the flow.

ACKNOWLEDGE the beneficial and the healthy, without judging it. ACKNOWLEDGE the harmful and the hurtful without judging it.

When you find yourself judging, let it drift out of your mind like a leaf being lifted by the wind.

Interpersonal Effectiveness

How to Ask for What You Want and Say "No" While Maintaining Self-Respect and Relationships with Others

Healthy/Hopeless Relationships

Directions: Letting go of hopeless relationships and building healthy ones is a critical component of a balanced life. This checklist is designed to help you identify your feelings in your current relationships and assist you in coming to a clear and beneficial conclusion. Put a check (✓) next to all statements that apply. The following worksheet provides steps to identify components within your relationship that add to its difficulty or whether there is a benefit in working to rebuild and strengthen a relationship.

	Resentment has built up
	You can talk openly
	You don't see your partner as important
	You cannot see a positive future in this relationship
	You are solution-focused in times of stress
	You are giving up or gave up on your partner
	Arguments escalate in intensity
	You feel taken for granted
	You feel hopeless about your relationship
	You constantly worry about whether the other person really cares about you
	You let others into your relationships (e.g., family, friends)
	You complain about the other person to everyone else but him or her
	You use passive-aggressive behavior to try and get needs met
	You are constantly questioning your relationship

Do you feel that this relationship is hopeless or worth trying to improve? (circle one)

Hopeless   Worth it

Steps to Conflict Resolution

Directions: Follow the steps below to resolve the conflict in your relationship (if you feel like it is worth saving).

Clearly state the problem:

- Describe it in terms of behaviors that are currently occurring or not occurring.
- Break problems down into smaller ones and deal with them individually.
- Both of you must agree on the problem and be willing to work on it.

Clarify the importance of the issue:

- Make clear why the issue(s) is important to you and provide your point of view on it
- Clarify your desires and what you would like to see considered in the solution..
- Do not offer specific solutions at this time.

Discuss potential solutions:

- Remain solution focused; the intent is not to defend yourself, decide who is right or wrong, or identify the truth about what happened in the past.
- The goal is to determine how to do things differently from now on.
- If a single or limited number of alternatives is available, consider problem-solving by generating a variety of possible solutions in a creative way.

Decide on mutual solution:

- Try to find a compromise that works for both of you.
- State your solution in clear, specific, behavioral terms.
- Do not accept a solution without intending to follow through.
- Do not accept a solution that makes you angry or resentful.

Try the solution for a specified time period:

- Allow time and opportunity to rework the solution if necessary.
- Review if it is beneficial for both of you at the end of the time period.

Wants-to-Shoulds Balance

Directions: Use the scale below to identify and distinguish between your wants and your shoulds. For example, you want to go out with your friends, but you should help you daughter with her homework. List all the wants and shoulds that you can think of and try to keep them in balance.

_____   _____

_____   _____

_____   _____

_____   _____

_____   _____

WANTS   **SHOULDS**

REMEMBER IT IS IMPORTANT TO KEEP THEM IN BALANCE BECAUSE:

It gets your opinions taken seriously.

It gets others, not just you, to do things.

Getting My Needs Met F-A-S-T

One of the guidelines for self-respect effectiveness is the concept of F-A-S-T, which stands for:

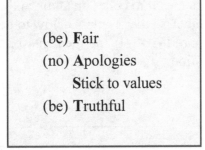

(be) **Fair**
(no) **Apologies**
     Stick to values
(be) **Truthful**

(be) Fair entails the client being fair to himself or herself and to the other person in his or her attempts to get his or her needs met. The central concept is that it is hard for the client to respect himself or herself over the long term if he or she consistently takes advantage of the other person.

(no) Apologies entails apologizing when apologies are warranted but not engaging in overly apologetic behavior. Your client should not be apologizing for being alive, for making the request, for having an opinion, or for disagreeing.

Stick to Values entails the client not compromising his or her values or integrity just to get what he or she wants or to keep the other person liking him or her. Your client is encouraged to be clear on what, in his or her opinion, is the moral or valued way of thinking and acting.

(be) Truthful entails the client not lying or acting helpless when he or she is not. He or she should not exaggerate or fall into a pattern of dishonesty. The client should be aware that one instance of dishonesty may not hurt, but dishonesty as a typical pattern erodes his or her self-respect over time. He or she is discouraged from acting helpless, as this is the opposite of building mastery.

Next Steps

The worksheet that follows is designed to help your client grasp this concept and implement it into his or her daily life. This is a challenge for many clients on the borderline or other personality disorder spectra. The client may need to use this worksheet on multiple occasions to master the skill of building and maintaining his or her self-respect.

Getting My Needs Met F-A-S-T

Directions: The concept of F-A-S-T is meant to help you attain and maintain your self-respect without giving away parts of yourself needlessly. Use the prompts below to describe various aspects of a specific situation. Next, read about the concept of F-A-S-T, and then answer some evaluative questions about how you handled the situation in question.

Triggering event:

_____

_____

_____

What do I want out of this situation?

_____

_____

_____

How do I want the other person to feel about me?

_____

_____

_____

How do I feel about myself in this situation?

_____

_____

_____

What I said or did in this situation:

_____

_____

_____

I was (circle one):   Assertive   Aggressive   Passive

Using assertiveness skills and not being passive or aggressive allows us to hold onto our self-respect when dealing with others. To hold onto our self-respect we need to be F-A-S-T about it:

> (be) **F**air
> (no) **A**pologies
>   **S**tick to values
> (be) **T**ruthful

Describe how you were FAIR with yourself and the other person:

_____

_____

_____

Were you able to make no APOLOGIES for making a request, having an opinion, or disagreeing?

Yes   No

Describe how you were able to STICK TO VALUES and hold your position, opinion, and not give in just to be liked:

_____

_____

_____

Were you able to be TRUTHFUL by not lying, not acting helpless if you were not, and not exaggerating?

Yes   No

How do you feel maintaining your self-respect and approaching the situation in a more authentic manner?

_____

_____

_____

Moving Beyond the Conflict: G-I-V-E

The concept of G-I-V-E helps with maintaining relationships. G-I-V-E entails:

> (be) **Gentle**
>
> (act) **Interested**
>
> **Validate**
>
> (use an) **Easy manner**

(be) Gentle entails the client responding to gentleness more than to harshness. He or she should avoid attacks, threats, and judgmental statements. He or she is discouraged from making statements such as "I'll kill myself if you ...." Your client is encouraged to tolerate a "no" to requests and to stay in the discussion even if it gets painful, then exit gracefully.

(act) Interested entails being interested in the other person. Your client is encouraged to listen to what the other person has to say, "share the air time," and not make it all about him or her. He or she does not interrupt or talk over the other person and is sensitive to the other person's desire to have the discussion at another time if that is what he or she wants.

Validate entails being outwardly nonjudgmental. Your client should validate the other person's feelings, wants, difficulties, and opinions about the situation. He or she is encouraged to find the "grain of truth" in what the other person is saying. This is a valuable skill to practice even if no conflict is present. More than any other skill, this one has the potential to affect the quality of relationships.

Use an Easy manner entails the client trying to be lighthearted, using a little humor and a smile. The goal is to ease the other person through the process. The central concept is that people do not like to be bullied, pushed around, or made to feel guilty.

Next Steps

The Moving Beyond the Conflict Worksheet is designed to help your client grasp this concept and implement it into his or her daily life. This is a challenge for many clients on the borderline and other personality disorder spectra, and may require that the client use this worksheet on multiple occasions to master the skill of building and maintaining his or her relationships.

Moving Beyond the Conflict: G-I-V-E

Directions: The concept of G-I-V-E is meant to help you keep relationships and enhance your influence in social situations. Use the prompts below to describe various aspects of a specific situation. Then you will answer some evaluative questions about how you handled the situation in question.

Triggering event:

_____

_____

_____

What do you want to get out of this interaction (goal)?

_____

_____

_____

When relationships do not go the way you expect, how do you tend to react (relationship)?

_____

_____

_____

When someone says something you do agree with, how do you tend to react (relationship)?

_____

_____

_____

What changes do you want the other person to make (goal)?

_____

_____

_____

How do you want to feel about yourself after the interaction (self-respect)?

_____

_____

_____

Rate from 1 (most important) to 3 (least important) how important each of the following is for you to get out of the triggering event?

_____ Goal   _____ Relationship   _____ Self-respect

To resolve conflicts and maintain relationships, we have to G-I-V-E:

(be) **G**entle
(act) **I**nterested
Validate
(use an) **E**asy Manner

How would you use a GENTLE manner in this situation? (no attacks, no threats, no judging)

_____

_____

_____

How would you act INTERESTED in this situation? (listen to the other person's point of view, reasons for saying "no," or for making a request of you)

_____

_____

_____

_____

How would you VALIDATE the other person's feelings, wants, difficulties, and opinions in this situation?

_____

_____

_____

_____

How would you use an EASY MANNER in this situation? (using a little humor, being light-hearted)

_____

_____

_____

_____

Get What You Want: D-E-A-R M-A-N

Directions: To get what you want in a stressful situation that triggers old aggressive or passive-aggressive behaviors, use the D-E-A-R M-A-N technique. Use this worksheet to do it differently.

> **D**escribe
> **E**xpress
> **A**ssert
> **R**einforce
>
> (stay) **M**indful
> **A**ppear confident
> **N**egotiate

DESCRIBE the trigger event: (tell the person exactly what you are reacting to)

_____

_____

_____

_____

How could you EXPRESS your feelings or opinions (use "I want," or "I don't want," instead of "I need," "You should," or "I can't") **most effectively in response to this trigger event?**

_____

_____

_____

How could you ASSERT yourself by asking for what you want and saying "no" clearly? (assume that others cannot read your mind and do not know how hard it is for you to ask directly for what you want)

_____

_____

_____

_____

How would you REINFORCE or reward the person ahead of time by explaining the positive effect of you getting what you want or need? (how could you reward them afterwards)

_____

_____

_____

_____

How could you stay MINDFUL and focused on your goal? (stay on your point, ignore attacks, threats, etc., or express your opinion continuously)

_____

_____

_____

_____

_____

How would you APPEAR CONFIDENT and effective? (use a confident voice and physical manner, make good eye contact)

_____

_____

_____

_____

_____

How would you NEGOTIATE to get what you want? (be willing to compromise, offer and ask for alternative solutions to the problem)

_____

_____

_____

_____

Emotion Regulation

How to Change Emotions That You Want to Change

Primary and Secondary Emotions

Primary and secondary emotions are confusing to many individuals, particularly those along the borderline spectrum or those with BPD. Primary emotions can be thought of as genuine or core emotions, and secondary emotions can be thought of as "learned" emotions. Marsha Linehan, creator of DBT, states that "dysfunctional and maladaptive responses to events are often connected or interwoven with 'authentic' or valid responses to events". In some instances, secondary emotions, such as fear, shame, and anger, are expressed even before the individual can understand and comprehend the primary emotions. Secondary emotions typically confuse the evaluation of the situation and, in many cases, the individual. The value of distinguishing and gaining greater understanding of primary and secondary emotions cannot be understated.

Next Steps

Primary and Secondary Emotions Worksheet is designed to make a distinction between primary and secondary emotions. It will cover triggering events, conditions in which the emotions are expressed and experienced, and the concluding behavior and outcome. This worksheet provides the client with an opportunity to gain insight and ultimately encourage the expression of his or her primary and authentic emotions. The client can be given several copies of the worksheet to fill out between sessions and use in real-world situations to encourage the authentic evaluation of the situations he or she experiences. The worksheet can then be brought into session and explored in treatment. An example is provided.

After your client has filled out the worksheet and you have identified the primary emotion that is motivating the behavior, you can use this information in treatment to help control the client's maladaptive reactions and lessen the impact of adverse situations. The worksheets in the DBT sections on mindfulness, interpersonal effectiveness, distress tolerance, and emotional regulation can be used to continue this treatment success.

Primary and Secondary Emotions

Emotion(s): *Anger, disgust, resentment*

Triggering event (please detail the event that caused you to feel this way): *Not getting what I wanted; people attacking my character when I did not get the day off I deserve.*

What were your thoughts about the triggering event that caused you to feel this way? *I will never get what I want; I am not important enough to get what I want; believing I am worthless and of no value.*

When we experience secondary emotions, we sometimes feel stuck, like in a spider's web. Being stuck makes it hard to get to the center, or to more authentic and primary emotions. You can see that the secondary emotions of anger, disgust, and resentment are caught in the web. They are making it difficult to recognize the primary emotions of hurt and fear, which are the authentic emotions driving your behavior. The inner section of the web is for the emotions that truly cause you to react in certain ways and act on certain urges when the emotion arises.

Describe your behavior when acting on the primary emotion(s) at the center of the emotional web: *Isolate myself from everyone; I become inactive; scream, yell, and get into fights with kids and significant other.*

What was the result of acting on this emotion? *People stay away from me because they know I will go off, but all I really want is someone to help me; cut myself or get high and end up in emergency room.*

Primary and Secondary Emotions

Directions: Follow the steps outlined below to help identify the emotions you felt in particular situations and which emotions are strongest to determine their influence on your behavior.

Emotion(s): _____

Triggering event (please detail the event that caused you to feel this way):

_____

_____

_____

_____

_____

_____

What were your thoughts about the triggering event that caused you to feel this way?

_____

_____

_____

_____

_____

_____

Use the emotional web to indicate your primary and secondary emotions. When we experience secondary emotions, we sometimes feel stuck, like in a spider's web. Being stuck makes it hard to get to the center, or to more authentic and primary emotions. The inner section of the web is for the emotions that truly cause you to react in certain ways and act on urges when the emotion arises. The outer sections of the web are for the secondary emotions.

Describe the behavior in which you engaged when acting on your emotion(s):

_____

_____

_____

_____

_____

_____

_____

What was the result of acting on this emotion?

_____

_____

_____

_____

_____

_____

_____

Acting Opposite Emotion

Directions: The primary emotions that drive individuals to act in inauthentic ways are fear, guilt or shame, sadness or depression, and anger. The table that follows illustrates each emotion, typical responses to each, and "acting opposite" behaviors that enable you to do things differently and increase the probability of a positive outcome. Answer the questions below.

Emotion	Response	Acting Opposite
Sadness/ depression	• Deactivate behavior • Attack self • Lessen self-confidence • Lessen competence	• Get active • Approach situation • Do not avoid • Engage in behaviors that make you feel competent and self-confident
Fear/anxiety	• Avoid situation • Not challenge cause of emotion • Disengage (inadvertently reinforced)	• Challenge situation • Engage in feared situation • Do what you fear repeatedly • Build control/mastery through behaviors
Guilt/shame	• Self-ridicule • Disengage • If unjustified, keep doing it • If justified, repair it, apologize, move on	• Do something nice for offended person (or someone else if that is not possible) • Commit to avoiding that mistake in the future
Anger	• Attack other or self • Act out toward self or other • Criticize self or other	• Identify cues and leave situation • Avoid other person instead of attacking • Do something nice not mean • Be sympathetic not blaming

Think of a situation that evoked one of the emotions listed above and describe the situation in as much detail as you can:

_____

_____

_____

Describe a typical response you engage in once you are emotionally evoked in the situation described above:

_____

_____

_____

List the acting opposite responses you could engage in to better manage the situation: (the more options you can provide the better)

_____

_____

To do things differently and act opposite, it is often helpful to have a motivational statement or quote to tell yourself. This motivational statement or quote should be positive and encouraging. Sample motivational statements are listed here. You can use these or find your own.

If you want to achieve greatness, stop asking for permission.

~Anonymous

Things work out best for those who make the best of how things work out.

~John Wooden

To live a creative life, we must lose our fear of being wrong.

~Anonymous

If you are not willing to risk the usual, you will have to settle for the ordinary.

~Jim Rohn

Trust because you are willing to accept the risk, not because it's safe or certain.

~Anonymous

Take up one idea. Make that one idea your life—think of it, dream of it, live on that idea. Let the brain, muscles, nerves, every part of your body, be full of that idea, and just leave every other idea alone. This is the way to success.

~Swami Vivekananda

All our dreams can come true if we have the courage to pursue them.

~Walt Disney

Good things come to people who wait, but better things come to those who go out and get them.

~Anonymous

If you do what you always did, you will get what you always got.

~Anonymous

Success is walking from failure to failure with no loss of enthusiasm.

~Winston Churchill

Just when the caterpillar thought the world was ending, he turned into a butterfly.

~Proverb

Successful entrepreneurs are givers and not takers of positive energy.

~Anonymous

Whenever you see a successful person, you only see the public glories, never the private sacrifices to reach them.

~Vaibhav Shah

Opportunities don't happen, you create them.

~Chris Grosser

Try not to become a person of success, but rather try to become a person of value.

~Albert Einstein

Great minds discuss ideas; average minds discuss events; small minds discuss people.

~Eleanor Roosevelt

I have not failed. I've just found 10,000 ways that won't work.

~Thomas A. Edison

If you don't value your time, neither will others. Stop giving away your time and talents—start charging for it.

~Kim Garst

A successful man is one who can lay a firm foundation with the bricks others have thrown at him.

~David Brinkley

No one can make you feel inferior without your consent.

~Eleanor Roosevelt

The whole secret of a successful life is to find out what is one's destiny to do, and then do it.

~Henry Ford

If you're going through hell, keep going.

~Winston Churchill

The ones who are crazy enough to think they can change the world, are the ones that do.

~Anonymous

Don't raise your voice, improve your argument.

~Anonymous

What seems to us as bitter trials are often blessings in disguise.

~ Oscar Wilde

The meaning of life is to find your gift. The purpose of life is to give it away.

~Anonymous

The distance between insanity and genius is measured only by success.

~Bruce Feirstein

When you stop chasing the wrong things you give the right things a chance to catch you.

~Lolly Daskal

Don't be afraid to give up the good to go for the great.

~John D. Rockefeller

No masterpiece was ever created by a lazy artist.

~Anonymous

Happiness is a butterfly, which when pursued, is always beyond your grasp, but which, if you will sit down quietly, may alight upon you.

~Nathaniel Hawthorne

Your own motivational statement:

_____

_____

Negative Emotional Resistance

Directions: This worksheet outlines the six keys to fighting susceptibility to negative emotions: PLEASE MASTER. Using each of these six components every day will help enhance your negative emotional resistance and increase the probability of maintaining control of yourself and the world around you.

> Treat **PhysicaL** Illness
>
> Balance **E**ating
>
> Avoid mood-**A**ltering Drugs
>
> Balance **S**leep
>
> Get **E**xercise
>
> Build **MASTER**y

Treat **PhysicaL** illness

How can you take care of your body?

_____

_____

_____

Balance **E**ating

What foods are good for you, and which should you stay away from?

_____

_____

_____

Avoid mood-**A**ltering drugs

What drugs do you need to avoid? (alcohol is considered a drug)

_____

_____

_____

Balance Sleep

How much sleep do you need each night to feel good? _____

What helps you sleep, and what prevents you from getting good sleep?

_____

_____

_____

_____

Get Exercise

What exercise could you do every day? (try to build up to 20 minutes each day)

_____

_____

_____

_____

Build MASTERy

What can you do every day to make yourself feel in control and competent?

_____

_____

_____

_____

Emotional Description

Directions: Observe and describe your current emotional state. Ask your therapist for the Emotions List if needed:

_____

_____

_____

EXPERIENCE YOUR EMOTION

> Do not PREVENT the emotion
>
> Do not COVER UP the emotion
>
> Do not try to AVOID the emotion
>
> Do not try to DEFLECT the emotion
>
> Do not try to HOLD ON to the emotion
>
> Do not try and STRENGTHEN the emotion

YOUR EMOTIONS DO NOT MAKE YOU WHO YOU ARE

> Do not JUDGE your emotion
>
> Practice EMOTIONAL COMPLIANCE
>
> Radically ACCEPT your emotion

Describe the triggering event related to this emotion:

_____

_____

_____

What are your beliefs and assumptions about the situation?

_____

_____

_____

Describe how your body feels and changes when you sense this emotion:

_____

_____

_____

Describe your body language from your face to your toes when you feel this way:

_____

_____

_____

What do you feel like doing when you feel this way?

_____

_____

_____

What did you say while feeling this way?

_____

_____

_____

What did you do while feeling this way?

_____

_____

_____

What do your mind and body feel like after you experience this emotion?

_____

_____

_____

Unhealthy to Healthy Coping

Directions: Following is a list of some unhealthy coping activities. Please put a check (✓) next to all that you engage in.

	Beating yourself up mentally
	Illegal drug use
	Prescription drug misuse or not taking drugs as prescribed/instructed
	Alcohol misuse
	Isolating yourself from other people
	Self-harm, self-mutilation, or deliberately inflicting pain on yourself
	Denying the problem exists
	Refusing to get professional help
	Addictive behaviors, such as gambling, Internet addiction, sexual addiction, thrill seeking or taking unnecessary risks, or any activity done to excess
	Overeating or undereating
	Burning bridges; e.g., cutting off friendships and other relationships, quitting jobs, and moving frequently
	Denying yourself playtime, rest, social interaction, fun, and other healthy human needs

Can you think of other unhealthy coping skills that you engage in?

_____

_____

When do you engage in these unhealthy coping mechanisms most often?

_____

_____

_____

100 Healthy Coping Activities

The following are 100 healthy coping activities. Which ones could you use instead of engaging in unhealthy coping activities. Circle all that apply.

1. Practice deep breathing—in through your nose, out through your mouth
2. Do a puzzle
3. Draw, paint, or color
4. Listen to uplifting or inspirational music
5. Blow bubbles
6. Squeeze an ice cube tightly
7. Go to the library
8. Visit the animal shelter
9. Pet your cat or dog
10. Clean or organize a space
11. Make your bed
12. Play a game on the computer
13. Turn on all the lights
14. Sit in the sun and close your eyes
15. Throw rocks into the woods
16. Suck on a peppermint
17. Chew gum
18. Sip a cup of hot chocolate or tea
19. Compliment someone
20. Read
21. Listen to inspirational tapes
22. Practice a relaxation exercise
23. Jump up and down
24. Write yourself a nice note and carry it in your pocket
25. Play solitaire
26. Do the dishes
27. Go for a brisk 10-minute walk
28. Dance to music
29. Call a friend
30. Invite a friend over
31. Organize your music collection
32. Write positive affirmations on notecards
33. Go outside and listen to nature
34. Go to the mall and people watch
35. Read a joke book
36. Volunteer
37. Offer to walk a neighbor's dog
38. Find a safe, quiet place to sit, and stay there until you know you can be safe
39. Look at pictures in a nature magazine
40. Write a list of compliments about a friend or teacher and give it to him or her
41. Work in the garden or flower bed
42. Plant a flower in a pot
43. Sew, knit, or crochet
44. Do yoga
45. Watch a funny or inspirational movie
46. Draw with sidewalk chalk
47. Make a collage with pictures of your favorite things
48. Make a collage showing a positive future
49. Journal
50. Write a poem
51. Paint your nails (not red or black)
52. Make a gratitude list
53. Scream into a pillow
54. Swim, run, jog, or bike

55. Jump rope

56. Smell a flower and touch the petals

57. Play a musical instrument

58. Do a good deed

59. Shoot hoops

60. Sing your favorite song out loud

61. Count backwards from 500

62. Brush your hair 100 times

63. Squeeze a stress ball

64. Use some good smelling lotion

65. Think of three foods for every letter or the alphabet without skipping any

66. Write down how you're feeling and why; read once, and put it away

67. Practice mindfulness—close your eyes and imagine yourself in a beautiful place and imagine how it smells, what you see, what you hear, what you feel

68. Write something positive about yourself for every letter of the alphabet and decorate it

69. Slowly eat one piece of your favorite candy

70. Write a letter to someone

71. Shred blank sheets of paper

72. Talk into a voice recorder

73. Play a board game with a friend or sibling

74. Go to the movies

75. Write poetry

76. Pray

77. Recite the serenity prayer

78. Print your favorite Bible verse on a card and memorize it

79. Decorate your locker

80. Decorate your mirror with positive affirmations and your favorite photos

81. Do a crossword, word search, or Sudoku puzzle

82. Visit an inspirational website (try www.values.com)

83. Write a thank you note to your best friend

84. Call a hotline

85. Put on your favorite outfit

86. Do your make-up

87. Read the comics

88. Draw a cartoon

89. String a necklace

90. Make friendship bracelets and give one to someone who looks lonely

91. Slowly sip a glass of cold water

92. Go on a walk and take photos of flowers with a cell phone or digital camera—challenge yourself to find 15 different kinds

93. Bite your pillow as hard as you can

94. Talk to a stuffed animal

95. Clean one room of your house

96. Ask a friend to meet you at the park

97. Wash and style your hair

98. Go to McDonalds and order an ice-cream cone from the dollar menu

99. Buy or check out a fun magazine and read it front to back

100. Window shop

Other: _____

_____

_____

_____

It is best to regularly use these healthy coping activities in your daily life so that when you do encounter stress, you are ready for it!

Distress Tolerance

How to Tolerate Pain in Difficult Situations, Not Change It

Accept to Surpass
(Radical Acceptance)

When in crisis and managing distress, use your WISE MIND (the balance of emotion and thought to reason in a situation), as it ACCEPTS the situation you have little or no control over.

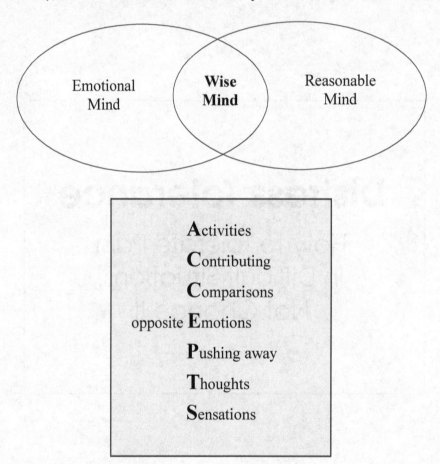

When distressed, do not engage, but distract yourself until you are calm and can approach the situation using a WISE MIND.

The key is to learn to tolerate crisis and not react with raw emotion, which can leave you feeling worse in most cases. The more you learn to tolerate a crisis, the stronger you will become.

Disengage and distract yourself with:

Activities: Exercise; hobbies; using your talents; watching a movie; or going to the park, zoo, or beach.

Contributing: Doing volunteer work, giving something to someone else, writing a letter to someone who is lonely, baking some cookies, or doing a surprising thoughtful thing.

Comparisons: Comparing yourself to people coping with problems that are the same or worse than yours, thinking of crises worse than yours, or remembering a time you were doing worse.

opposite **E**motions: Reading a book, listening to music, or watching shows and movies that impact you emotionally. If sad, watch a comedy; if scared, watch something daring and exciting; if angry, listen to calm, relaxing music.

Pushing away: Putting the crisis out of your mind, imagining a volume knob being turned down, or imagining a balloon of stress deflating.

Thoughts: Filling your brain with other thoughts so you do not think about the crisis, playing a word puzzle game on your phone or computer, or counting to 200 by 7s.

Sensations: Holding an ice cube in your hand, putting some Pop Rocks in your mouth, taking a cold or hot shower, eating a small piece of chocolate and letting it melt in your mouth, or going inside if you are outside or vice versa.

Which of these strategies would work for you?

_____

_____

_____

DBT: Distress Tolerance
Proof of Survival

When in crisis, IMPROVE the moment to survive it. Remember that getting through it provides proof that you can and will survive.

> Imagery
>
> Meaning
>
> Prayer
>
> Relaxation
>
> One thing in the moment
>
> Vacation
>
> Encouragement

Imagery: Imagine a place you feel happy, safe, relieved, and relaxed. This can be a beach, an open field, a place with or without doors, or the ocean with calm waves.

Meaning: What is the value, purpose, or meaning in the crisis? "There is no growth without dissonance." Find positive aspects of the crisis and think about how getting through this experience helps you.

Prayer: Use and connect to religious or spiritual rituals that have personal meaning. Ask for strength to bear the moment.

Relaxation: Use progressive relaxation: One by one, tense each muscle and part of your body for 7 seconds, then release it. Try yoga, meditation, or any other form of exercise that relaxes you.

One thing in the moment: Focus all of your attention on the here and now. Stay present in your body and on your movements.

Vacation: Deliberately step away from your life to do something relaxing and enjoyable. Stay in bed for 20 minutes under the covers, get take-out instead of cooking, or spend quiet time not talking to anyone for 1 hour.

Encouragement: Be your own cheerleader! Repeat positive self-statements, such as "I can do it," "I can handle this," or "I can only do what I can do."

What imagery can you use to improve your mood?

_____

_____

What is the meaning in the crisis?

_____

_____

What prayer or spiritual thought helps you get through?

_____

_____

Progressive Muscle Relaxation
Foot (curl your toes on one foot downward for 7 seconds, then release)
Lower leg and foot (tighten your calf muscle in one leg by pulling toes toward you for 7 seconds, then release)
Entire leg (squeeze thigh muscles in one leg for 7 seconds while doing above, then release)   _(Repeat on other side of body)_
Hand (clench one fist for 7 seconds, then release)
Entire arm (tighten your biceps in one arm by drawing your forearm up toward your shoulder and "making a muscle," while clenching your fist for 7 seconds, then release)   _(Repeat on other side of body)_
Buttocks (tighten by pulling your buttocks together for 7 seconds, then release)
Stomach (suck your stomach in for 7 seconds, then release)
Chest (tighten by taking a deep breath for 7 seconds, then release)
Neck and shoulders (raise your shoulders up to touch your ears for 7 seconds, then release)
Mouth (open your mouth wide enough to stretch the hinges of your jaw for 7 seconds, then release)
Eyes (clench your eyelids tightly shut for 7 seconds, then release)
Forehead (raise your eyebrows as far as you can for 7 seconds, then release)

Where did you go or what did you do on your private vacation?

_____

_____

What is your encouragement statement?

_____

_____

You have made it this far, that is PROOF of SURVIVAL and proof that you can continue to do it!

Four Keys to Crisis Survival

> To be free of suffering requires **ACCEPTANCE** deep inside yourself

> Make the **CHOICE** to accept reality as it is

> Be **WILLING** to do what is needed in each situation

> Replace **WILLFULNESS** with **WILLINGNESS**

Directions: Answer the following questions.

What are you fighting to accept?

_____

_____

What is it about the reality of the crisis that you refuse to accept?

_____

_____

What choice could you make to change the crisis?

_____

_____

What does your gut tell you to do to manage this crisis, and are you willing to do it?

_____

_____

How does your willfulness show? (e.g., giving up, refusing to engage, refusing to make needed changes)

_____

_____

Are you willing to make the change? (circle one)

Yes   No

Accepting Reality

Blocks to accepting reality include the following:

Anger and Resentment
• Holding anger makes you falsely believe you are punishing the offending person
• Holding anger and resentment makes you incorrectly think the other person is not getting away with offending you
• Anger and resentment serve as a reminder of the pain the other person caused you

Disagreement
• Refusing to agree means you falsely believe you still have power and control over the offending person and situation
• You refuse to accept the situation and agree to show you do not approve of the offending person or situation

Encourage Suffering
• Your suffering makes you falsely feel protected to never forget how you were offended
• Suffering makes you incorrectly think you are showing the offending person how much he or she hurt you
• Suffering is misused as a distraction from the reality of the situation

Your *true freedom and power* come from
Radical Acceptance of reality and making a choice to

DO IT DIFFERENTLY

Accepting Reality

Directions: Answer the following questions.

What reality am I refusing to accept?

_____

_____

_____

_____

_____

What blockades am I using? (circle all that apply)

Anger and Resentment   Disagreement   Encourage Suffering

What behaviors do I engage in to promote my refusal to accept?

_____

_____

_____

_____

_____

How do I benefit from refusing to accept?

_____

_____

_____

_____

_____

What can I control in this situation?

_____

_____

_____

_____

_____

If I accepted the situation, how would I feel?

_____

_____

_____

_____

_____

Can you see that acceptance relieves suffering by allowing you to let go? (circle one)

Yes   No

Do you agree that pain creates suffering when you refuse to accept the pain? (circle one)

Yes   No

Can you see that acceptance is not complying with the offending person and situation, but giving yourself power and control by releasing yourself from it? (circle one)

Yes   No

Acceptance is a fork in the road. You can choose to continue your anger, disagreement, and suffering or choose reality, power, and self-control.

Anger   Reality
Disagreement   ⟵ Radical ⟶   Power
Suffering   Acceptance   Self-control

Willingness Over Willfulness

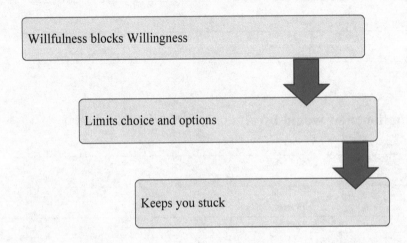

Willfulness blocks Willingness

Limits choice and options

Keeps you stuck

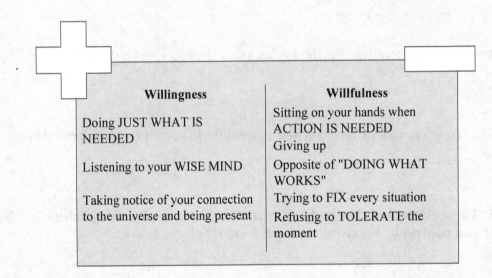

Willingness	Willfulness
Doing JUST WHAT IS NEEDED	Sitting on your hands when ACTION IS NEEDED
Listening to your WISE MIND	Giving up
	Opposite of "DOING WHAT WORKS"
Taking notice of your connection to the universe and being present	Trying to FIX every situation
	Refusing to TOLERATE the moment

Directions: Answer the following questions.

When I am being WILLFUL, I feel (ask your therapist for the Emotions List, if needed):

_____

_____

_____

_____

Draw what your body and face look like when you are being WILLFUL:

In what situations do you become WILLFUL?

_____
_____
_____
_____

My WILLINGNESS feels like:

_____
_____
_____
_____

The best way for me to show my WILLINGNESS is by:

_____
_____
_____
_____

References

For your convenience, you may download a pdf version of the worksheets in this book from our dedicated website:

go.pesi.com/fox

American Psychiatric Association. (1980). *Diagnostic and statistical manual of mental disorders*, 3rd ed. Washington, D.C.: American Psychiatric Association.

American Psychiatric Association. (2013). *Diagnostic and Statistical Manual of Mental Disorders*, 5th ed. Washington, D.C.: American Psychiatric Association.

Bartholomew, K., & Horowitz, L. M. (1991). Attachment styles among young adults: A test of a four-category model. *Journal of Personality and Social Psychology*, *61*(2), 226–244.

Benjamin, L. S. (1987). Commentary on the inner experience of the borderline self-mutilator. *Journal of Personality Disorders, 1*, 334–339.

Benjamin, L. S. (1996). *Interpersonal diagnosis and treatment and personality disorders,* 2nd ed. New York, NY: Guilford Press.

Black, D. W., Gunter, T., Loveless, P., Allen, J., & Sieleni, B. (2010). Antisocial personality disorder in incarcerated offenders: Psychiatric comorbidity and quality of life. *Annals of Clinical Psychiatry*, *22* (2), 113–120.

Bowlby, J. (1988). *A secure base: Clinical applications of attachment theory.* London: Routledge.

Bukstein, O. G., Brent, D. A., Perper, J. A., Moritz, G., Baugher, M., Schweers, J., Roth, C., & Balach, L. (1993). Risk factors for completed suicide among adolescents with a lifetime history of substance abuse: A case-control study. *Acta Psychiatrica Scandinavica, 88*, 403–408.

Deltito, J., Martin L., Riefkohl, J., Austria, B., Kissilenko, A., Corless, C., & Morse, P. (2001). Do patients with borderline personality disorder belong to the bipolar spectrum? *Journal of Affective Disorders, 67*, 221–228.

Dickinson, K. A., & Pincus, A. L. (2003). Interpersonal analysis of grandiose and vulnerable narcissism. *Journal of Personality Disorders*, *17*(3), 188–207.

Fonagy, P., Target, M., Steele, M., Steele, H., Leigh, T., Levinson, A., & Kennedy, R. (1997). Morality, disruptive behavior, borderline personality disorder, crime and their relationship to security of attachment. In L. Atkinson & K. J. Zucker (Eds.), *Attachment and psychopathology* (pp. 223–274). New York, NY: Guilford Press.

Fox, D. (2013). *The clinician's guide to the diagnosis and treatment of personality disorders.* Eau Claire, WI: PESI Publishing and Media.

Frances, A. J., Fyer, M. R., & Clarkin, J. (1986). Personality and suicide. In J. J. Mann & M. Stanley (Eds.), *Annals of the New York Academy of Sciences: Vol. 487. Psychobiology of suicidal behavior* (pp. 281–293). New York: New York Academy of Sciences.

Freud, S. (1910). The origin and development of psychoanalysis. *American Journal of Psychology*, *21*, 181–218.

Frodi, A., Dernevik, M., Sepa, A., Philipson, J., & Bragesjö, M. (2001). Current attachment representations of incarcerated offenders varying in degree of psychopathy. *Attachment & Human Development. Special Issue: Attachment in Mental Health Institutions*, *3*(3), 269–283.

Gilligan, J. (1996). *Violence: Our deadly epidemic and its causes.* New York: G. P. Putnam's Sons.

Goldberg, J. F., & Garno, J. L. (2009). Age at onset of bipolar disorder and risk for comorbid borderline personality disorder. *Bipolar Disorders*, *11*(2), 205–208.

Hare, R. (1998). Psychopaths and their nature: Implications for the mental health and criminal justice systems. In T. Millon, E. Simonsen, M. Birket-Smith, & R. D. Davis (Eds.), *Psychopathy: antisocial, criminal, and violent behavior* (pp. 188–212). New York: Guilford.

Hare, R. D., Clark, D., Grann, M., & Thornton, D. (2000). Psychopathy and the predictive validity of the PCL-R: An international perspective. *Behavioral Sciences and the Law*, *18*, 623–645.

Hooley, J. M., & Wilson-Murphy, M. (2012). Adult attachment to transitional objects and borderline personality. *Journal of Personality Disorders*, *26*(2), 179–191.

Huang, Y., Kotov, R., de Girolamo, G., Preti, A., Angermeyer, M., Benjet, C., Demyttenaere, K., et al. (2009) *British Journal of Psychiatry*, *195*, 46–53. doi: 10.1192/bjp.bp.108.058552.

Huff, C. (2004). Where personality goes awry. *Monitor on Psychology*, *35*, 42.

Klonsky, E. D., Oltmanns, T. F., & Turkheimer, E. (2003). Deliberate self-harm in a nonclinical population: Prevalence and psychological correlates. *American Journal of Psychiatry*, *160*(8), 1501–1508.

Lenzenweger, M. F. (2010). Current status of the scientific study of the personality disorders: An overview of epidemiological, longitudinal, experimental psychopathology, and neurobehavioral perspectives. *Journal of the American Psychoanalytic Association*, *58*, 741–748.

Lenzenweger, M. F., Lane, M. C., Loranger, A. W., & Kessler, R. C. (2007). DSM-IV personality disorders in the National Comorbidity Survey Replication. *Biological Psychiatry*, *62*, 553–564.

Linehan, M. M. (1993). Cognitive-behavioral treatment of borderline personality disorder. Diagnosis and treatment of mental disorders. New York, NY US: Guilford Press.

Lion, J. R. (1987). Clinical assessment of violent patients. In L. Roth (Ed.), *Clinical treatment of the violent person* (pp. 1–19). New York: Guilford Press.

Loeber, R., Keenan, K., Lahey, B. B., Green, S. M., & Thomas, C. (1993). Evidence for developmentally based diagnoses of oppositional defiant disorder and conduct disorder. *Journal of Abnormal Child Psychology*, *21*, 377–410.

Lowen, A. (1985). *Narcissism: Denial of the true self.* New York: Macmillan.

Lykken, D. T. (1995). *Antisocial personalities.* Mahwah, NJ: Lawrence Erlbaum Associates.

Lykken, D. T. (2006). Theoretical and empirical foundations. In C. J. Patrick (Ed.), *Handbook of psychopathy* (pp. 3–13). New York, NY: Guilford Press.

MacDonald, J. M. (1963). The threat to kill. *American Journal of Psychiatry, 120*, 125–130.

MacKinnon, D. F., & Pies, R. (2006). Affective instability as rapid cycling: Theoretical and clinical implications for borderline personality and bipolar spectrum disorders. *Bipolar Disorders, 8*(1), 1–14.

Meloy, J.R. (2001). The mark of cain: psychoanalytic insight and the psychopath. Hillsdale, NJ: Aronson.

Miller, W. R., & Rollnick, S. (2002). *Motivational interviewing: Preparing people for change*, 2nd Ed. New York, NY: Guilford Press.

Millon, T., Millon, C. M., Grossman, S., Meagher, S., & Ramnath, R. (2004). *Personality disorders in modern life*. New York, NY: John Wiley & Sons.

Munsey, C. (2008). A well lived life. *Monitor on Psychology, 39*, 39.

Oldham, J. M., Gabbard, G. O., Goin, M. K., Gunderson, J., Soloff, P., Spiegal, D., Stone, M., & Phillips, K. A. (2010). *Practice guideline for the treatment of patients with borderline personality disorder.* Washington, D.C.: American Psychiatric Association.

Patrick, C. J. (2006). *The Handbook of Psychopathy*. New York, NY: Guildford Press.

Personality disorders. *Mental Health America*. Retrieved from http://www.nmha.org/go/information/get-info/personality-disorders

Ruggero, C. J, Zimmerman, M., Chelminski, I., & Young, D. (2010). Borderline personality disorder and the misdiagnosis of bipolar disorder. *Journal of Psychiatric Research, 44*, 405–408.

Silk, K. R. Personality disorders. *UpToDate*. Retrieved from http://www.uptodate.com/contents/personality-disorders?source=search_result&search=personality+disorders&selectedTitle=1~150

Steinmetz, D., & Tabenkin, H. (2001). The "difficult patient" as perceived by family physicians. *Family Practice, 18*, 495–500.

Staying well when you have a mental health condition. *Mental Health America*. Retrieved from http://www.nmha.org/go/mental-health-month/staying-well-when-you-have-a-mental-illness

Stinson, F. S., Dawson, D. A., Goldstein, R. B., Chou, S. P., Huang, B., Smith, S. M., Ruan, W.J., et al. (2008). Prevalence, correlates, disability, and comorbidity of DSM-IV narcissistic personality disorder: Results from the wave 2 national epidemiologic survey on alcohol and related conditions. *Journal of Clinical Psychology, 69*(7), 1033–1045.

Thomas, D. (2010). *Narcissism: Behind the mask*. Hove, UK: The Book Guild, Ltd.

Verona, E., Patrick, C. J., & Joiner, T. E. (2001). Psychopathy, antisocial personality, and suicide risk. *Journal of Abnormal Psychology, 110*, 462–470.

Wink, P. (1991). Two faces of narcissism. *Journal of Personality and Social Psychology, 61*, 590–597.

Zoccolillo, M., Pickles, A., Quinton, D., & Rutter, M. (1992). The outcome of conduct disorder: Implications for defining adult personality disorder and conduct disorder. *Psychological Medicine, 22*, 971–986.

Appendix A

Cluster B Client Assessment Scoring (p.6)

Scoring: Use the scale below to quantify your answers. Score all four Cluster B personality disorders. Write the score for the response below the question number from the worksheet in the table. A total score of 7 or higher suggests that the person has that personality disorder or related traits. The highest score indicates which disorder or significant number of traits is/are prominent. Two equivalent scores may indicate comorbidity.

0 = Never, 1 = Past, 2 = Present

Personality Disorder	Question Number							Total Score
Antisocial Personality Disorder	1	5	8	14	19	23	26	
Narcissistic Personality Disorder	2	13	16	18	20	22	27	
Histrionic Personality Disorder	4	7	10	12	17	24	25	
Borderline Personality Disorder	3	6	9	11	15	21	28	

ASPD or related traits = 7 or greater
NPD or related traits = 7 or greater
HPD or related traits = 7 or greater
BPD or related traits = 7 or greater

The Next Step: Once you have determined the highest score(s) for your client, go to the section related to that disorder in the workbook. For example, if your client's highest score was a 10 borderline personality disorder, go to the section related to borderline personality disorder for worksheets relevant to issues that client may be experiencing.

Critical Factors in Treatment Answer Key (p.12)

Now that you have marked what etiological experience your client is likely to have had, compare your answers with answers provided in the following table.

Answer Key

Histrionic Personality Disorder	Sexual abuse, neglect, and deliberate self-harm
Antisocial Personality Disorder	Physical and emotional abuse, neglect, being bullied, bullying others, deliberate self-harm, and prolonged periods of misery
Narcissistic Personality Disorder	Neglect and being bullied
Borderline Personality Disorder	Sexual, physical, and emotional abuse, neglect, bullying others, deliberate self-harm, and prolonged periods of misery

Perception Questionnaire Scoring (p.39)

Scoring: The odd-numbered questions (1, 3, 5, 7, …) are related to the antisocial spectrum risk factors for suicide, whereas even-numbered questions (2, 4, 6, 8, …) are related to protective factors. Give each response of "Agree" one point and a response of "Disagree" no points. Count up the number of items that have been answered "Agree" for the suicide risk factors (odd-numbered questions) and "Disagree" for the protective factors (even-numbered questions).

Countertransference Scale Scoring (p.58)

Scoring: Give 1 point for each response that corresponds to the answer key below to determine the risk of countertransference.

Scoring Key for Countertransference Scale	
1. No	11. Yes
2. No	12. Yes
3. Yes	13. No
4. Yes	14. Yes
5. Yes	15. No
6. No	16. No
7. Yes	17. Yes
8. Yes	18. Yes
9. No	19. No
10. Yes	20. Yes

1–12: Good management of countertransference.

13–16: Fair management of countertransference.

17–20: Poor management of countertransference.

Self and Other Worksheet Scoring (p.65)

Scoring: Use the keys below to determine where your client is along the narcissistic spectrum. Give 1 point for each response that corresponds to the answer key below. A score of 3 to 5 within each factor is considered an indicator that your client meets criteria for this factor. Score all four narcissistic factors along the spectrum. It is important to note that as the individual moves along the narcissistic spectrum, he or she will meet criteria for the factor before it, as it is a cumulative process. For example, if your client is at the self-absorption level, he or she will score a 3 to 5 on the previous two narcissistic spectrum factors (self-confidence and self-preoccupation) as well.

Self-Confidence
1. A
2. A
3. A
4. A
5. B

Self-Preoccupation
6. A
7. A
8. A
9. B
10. A

Self-Absorption
11. A
12. B
13. A
14. A
15. A

Narcissism
16. B
17. A
18. A
19. A
20. B

Self-Confidence → Self-Preoccupation → Self-Absorption → Narcissistic Personality Disorder

Harm to Self and Other Worksheet Scoring (p.68)

Scoring: Use the key that follows to score your client's answers. Give 1 point for every "Yes" answer and use the criteria below to determine areas of concern. Please be sure to pay special attention to **question 8**, which is related to current suicidal ideation.

Suicide = 2, 4, 8, 11

Narcissistic injury = 1, 3, 5, 7, 9, 13

Harm to others = 6, 10, 12, 14

Once you have scored all three factors, determine whether your client has incurred a narcissistic injury and if he or she is considering harm to self or others. Utilize this information in session to explore how the client's view of himself or herself has changed, identify the triggering incident (you may wish to use the Narcissism Key Target Areas for Treatment Worksheet (In Part 4) to assist you in doing this), and determine how he or she plans to repair his or her self-esteem and/or self-worth.

Distinction Between Borderline Spectrum and Bipolar Disorder (p.144)

The table below has check marks next to the distinguishing characteristics between borderline personalty disorder and bipolar disorder. Use this to compare your responses to the check marks next to the characteristics in your client from the checklist.

Borderline	Bipolar	Characteristic
✓		Intensive efforts to avoid being alone
✓		Pattern of unstable/intense interpersonal relationships
✓		Disturbance in core self and self-identity
✓		Recurrent suicidal behavior, threats, gestures, or self-mutilating behavior in response to stressor or end of relationship.
	✓	Mood episodes are more discrete and longer acting and can often present without any obvious trigger
	✓	Symptoms present in episodes that are a change from the person's typical behavior
	✓	Impulsivity is only seen during a period of elevated mood, hypomanic or manic (without identifiable trigger).
✓		Paranoia or dissociation is short lived, without the development of long-term delusions or hallucinations
	✓	Delusions and hallucinations are present only during a depressed, manic, or mixed episode

Appendix B

Emotions List

Absorbed	Admiring	Adrift	Afraid
Aggravated	Alarmed	Alienated	Amazed
Ambivalent	Amused	Angry	Anguished
Annoyed	Anticipating	Anxious	Apologetic
Apprehensive	Aroused	Attraction	Awkward
Bitter	Bored	Brave	Calm
Caring	Comfortable	Compassionate	Concerned
Confident	Confused	Contemptuous	Curious
Delighted	Depressed	Disappointed	Disgraced
Disgusted	Disliked	Dismayed	Disoriented
Disturbed	Eager	Elated	Embarrassed
Enthusiastic	Envious	Exasperated	Exhausted
Exhilarated	Fearful	Frustrated	Glad
Grief-stricken	Grumpy	Guilty	Happy
Helpless	Hesitant	Hopeful	Hopeless
Horrified	Humiliated	Hurt	Indifferent
Infatuated	Insecure	Insulted	Interested
Intrigued	Irritated	Isolated	Jealous
Liked	Lonely	Loved	Lustful
Melancholy	Mocked	Neglected	Nervous
Numb	Optimistic	Overwhelmed	Panicked
Pity	Pleased	Preoccupied	Regretful
Rejected	Relaxed	Relieved	Resentful
Restless	Revulsion	Sad	Safe
Scared	Self-conscious	Shamed	Shocked
Sorrowful	Spiteful	Stunned	Tender
Trusting	Trusting	Uncertain	Uncomfortable
Vengeful	Weary	Worried	Wounded